S0-BDG-554

CHICAGO PUBLIC LIBRARY
HAROLD WASHINGTON LIBRARY CENTER

Ecological Studies

Analysis and Synthesis

Edited by

J. Jacobs, München · O. L. Lange, Würzburg
J. S. Olson, Oak Ridge · W. Wieser, Innsbruck

Volume 13

Epidemics of Plant Diseases
Mathematical Analysis and Modeling

Edited by Jürgen Kranz

With 46 Figures

Springer-Verlag   New York Heidelberg Berlin 1974

Professor Dr. JÜRGEN KRANZ, Tropeninstitut der Justus-Liebig-Universität, 6300 Gießen, Schottstraße 2–4/Federal Republic of Germany

REF
SB
731
.K7
cop.1

Library of Congress Cataloging in Publication Data

Kranz, Jürgen.
Epidemics of plant diseases.

(Ecological studies, v. 13)
Includes bibliographies.
1. Plant diseases. 2. Epidemiology—Mathematical models.
I. Title. II. Series.
SB731.K7   632   74-13821

ISBN 0-387-06896-1 Springer-Verlag New York · Heidelberg · Berlin
ISBN 3-540-06896-1 Springer-Verlag Berlin · Heidelberg · New York
ISBN 0-412-13650-3 Chapman & Hall Limited London

This work is subject to copyright. All rights are reserved, whether the whole or part of the material is concerned, specifically those of translation, reprinting, re-use of illustrations, broadcasting, reproduction by photocopying machine or similar means, and storage in data banks.

The use of registered names, trademarks, etc. in this publication does not imply, even in the absence of a specific statement, that such names are exempt from the relevant protective laws and regulations and therefore free for general use.

Under § 54 of the German Copyright Law where copies are made for other than private use, a fee is payable to the publisher, the amount of the fee to be determined by agreement with the publisher.

© by Springer-Verlag Berlin · Heidelberg 1974. Printed in Germany. Type-setting, printing, and binding: Brühlsche Universitätsdruckerei Gießen.

NOV   1 1976

Preface

During the past decade epidemiology has developed beyond the simple desription of ecological factors affecting disease. Population dynamics has become a major item of research, which in turn has prompted new approaches and philosophy. Though basically an empirical science, epidemiology has of necessity veered towards mathematical methods and modeling.

The growing importance of epidemiology was acknowledged by the organizers of the 2nd International Congress of Plant Pathology, held in Minneapolis in September 1973. One of the symposia was devoted to a discussion of the role of mathematics and modeling in the analysis of epidemics. The speakers considered that it would be valuable to expand their contributions for publication.

The following chapters give an outline of the record of achievement to date in the use of mathematical analysis and computer techniques in the study of epidemics of plant diseases; at the same time they seek to indicate the greatly enlarged possibilities, still in the early stages of investigation, of constructive work on this basis used in the field of epidemiology. A good beginning has been made in clarifying the very complex and sometimes confusing data by means of mathematical models and equations, and later by computer simulations. In this book practical procedures, such as experiments in coding techniques, reduction of data, computer programs, the particular scope of multiple regression analysis in the study of the progress of epidemics, disease increase and severity, disease cycles and crop losses, are variously discussed. Mathematical models and simulation models are presented, new suggestions made, and some of the main practical experiences and problems in the building and use of a simulator up to the present time are reported.

This book is primarily addressed to the plant pathologist and to the ecologist, who, it is hoped, will be stimulated to engage in this promising but relatively unfamiliar field of research, but also in the hope that the presented material, as yet only a beginning, may open the way to new knowledge in prediction and control of plant epidemics, which is of vital importance to our environment.

The editor feels indebted to this colleagues and gratefully acknowledges their willing and fruitful collaboration which has made this publication possible. Thanks are also due to Mrs. CHRISTA WIESNER for her assistance in the preparation of the manuscript.

Gießen, Summer 1974   J. KRANZ

Contents

Chapter II

Automatic Data Processing in Analyses of Epidemics
  M. MOGK

Chapter III

Multiple Regression Analysis in the Epidemiology of Plant Diseases
  D. J. BUTT and D. J. ROYLE

Chapter IV

Non-linear Disease Progress Curves
   D. Jowett, J. A. Browning and Blanche Cournoyer Haning

Chapter V

Simulation of Epidemics
   P. E. Waggoner

List of Authors

BROWNING, J. A.   Botany and Plant Pathology, Iowa State University, Ames, IA 50010/USA

BUTT, D. J.   East Malling Research Station, Maidstone, Kent, United Kingdom

COURNOYER HANING, BLANCHE   Dekalb Agric. Research, Dekalb, IL 60115/USA

JOWETT, D.   Ecosystems Analysis, University of Wisconsin, Green Bay, WI 54305/USA

KRANZ, J.   Tropeninstitut, Abt. Phytopathologie, Justus Liebig-Universität, D-6300 Gießen, Federal Republic of Germany

MOGK, M.   Tropeninstitut, Abt. Phytopathologie, Justus Liebig-Universität, D-6300 Gießen, Federal Republic of Germany

ROYLE, D. J.   Wye College (University of London), Wye near Ashford, Kent, United Kingdom

WAGGONER, P. E.   The Connecticut Agric. Experimental Station, Box 1106, New Haven, CT 06504/USA

Introduction

J. KRANZ

Epidemiology is the science of populations of pathogens in populations of hosts, and the disease resulting therefrom under the influence of the environment and human interferences (KRANZ, 1973). It is thus the science of disease dynamics in natural states. Diseases and their epidemics can here be regarded as systems, e.g. "interlocking complexes of processes characterized by many reciprocal cause-effect pathways" (WATT, 1966), regulated by feedback or rather intricate interactions.

An epidemic is the progress of disease y in time and space. This comprises the classical epidemic (e.g. steep rise and fall of disease incidence within a limited period) as well as any increase or decrease within the range $0 < y \leqq 1$. Epidemics are complex, with numerous factors involved, as in ecological systems, of which they are specific cases. As the majority of plant diseases are infectious diseases, their epidemics invariably depend on a regular chain of events. These events are elements and their relations are structures in the sense of systems analysis.

As plant pathologists are primarily concerned with plant populations, and as pathogens and their host exist in time, and are distributed in space, time and spatial effects become essential features of epidemics. They are also characterized by random processes and fluctuations, recurrence, as well as thresholds, limits and discontinuities. These are population phenomena which as such require mathematics, and which lend themselves to computer language. Moreover, computers are indispensable in handling the often vast and confused data.

Epidemiology, however, is not just an esoteric niche for mathematically-minded plant pathologists. Many experimenters who have no interest in, or even abhor, mathematics will continue to work on vital epidemiological issues. However, if their data are not just to be dumped, they have to resort to models, and for any quantitative and objective analysis, mathematics becomes obligatory. Only then can plant pathologists "... understand the structure and operation of the natural dynamic system ..." (MOTT, 1966). It would thus be ideal if every experimenter were also competent to make adequate use of mathematical methods. This could enrich the fruitful feedback between experiments and theory, which must prevail as a prominent feature in epidemiology.

Epidemiology has primarily to provide plant pathologists with refined and deepened knowledge of the behavior of diseases in the field. A better optimization of all control measures and a more efficient control strategy is the ultimate objective: "Chemical industry and plant breeders forge fine tactical weapons; but only epidemiology sets the strategy" (VAN DER PLANK, 1963). This objective is to secure food production and/or farmers' income, which often makes chemical control inevitable, and to satisfy a pollution-conscious public. With these obligations becoming increasingly acute, epidemiology will have to occupy a paramount position within future plant pathology (KRANZ, 1973). It is against this background that the topics of the following papers have to be viewed.

Models are needed to achieve these ends. What are models? One may distinguish between models and analogs. An analog "is any device or object in which entities are related to one another" (KACSER, 1960). Thus the controlled growth chamber is an analog of the environment in which a plant disease occurs. A spore trap is an analog of host surfaces, and a tetrahedron depicts distribution of propagules in the soil (BAKER, 1965). An appropriately programed computer must also be considered as an analog of disease. Analog, in brief, may be regarded as instrumental models. They are often built with simple elements in which quantities can be related in a functional form (for example: analog computer) or arithmetical form (digital computer) and they help to verify hypotheses which cannot otherwise be tackled. An analog may consequently also serve in building models.

The term "model" definitely contains a diversity of meanings, and the number of models is certainly as great as their degree of complexity and usefulness. A model may be a verbal statement, such as GARRETT'S (1960) inoculum potential, a particular course of daily climatic events to which a disease is exposed in a growth chamber to produce a "mini-epidemic" (COHEN and ROTEM, 1971), or a heuristic formula, a more or less sophisticated and complicated mathematical equation for the description, prediction and simulation of an epidemic. It may also be the set of biological parameters of a computer program called a "simulator".

Though all models have essentially the same logical status (KACSER, 1960), they can be of tentative or preliminary nature. Models may be a "working hypothesis", or even a real hypothesis, a theory or a law (though a law is a model, not every model is necessarily a law). A model is, in any case, an abstraction of the real world, a simplified approximation to reality (or parts of it), but by no means the reality itself, nor its replica. This implies that a model is rarely complete, final and an objective in itself. Every model is based on previous experiences or experiments and must be verified again and improved by experimentation. Experimental verification may, however, be impaired owing either to the limits of experimental accuracy (EDWARDS, 1960), or to the lack of suitable methods or equipment.

Models discipline research and organize knowledge, thus serving as deductive or inductive concepts to further scientific progress by means of experiments. Understanding and communication of phenomena would also be severely handicapped without models. This is the domain of heuristic or conceptual models. Models can, however, also be of immediate practical use for disease prediction and control.

A complex system like epidemics can be studied by modeling its elements as subsystems representing basic components with more or less common properties. This may be supplemented by more specific components until only components completely unique to one epidemic are left. This procedure enables us to cope with the great diversity of epidemics. We should add here that the same phenomenon may, of course, be explained by various models. And it is obvious that the particular model chosen has a definite influence on the experimental result. Competing or even contradictory models for the same phenomenon should be carefully studied before adopting any one of them. This may well be rewarding for the advancement of science.

There are a number of mathematical models known in biology in spite of the widespread reluctance amongst biologists to accept mathematics. One of the oldest mathematical models is that of segregation in genetics, basically a model of probability (EDWARDS, 1960; HARRIS, 1960), of great importance in the study of populations and evolutionary changes. Mathematical models may be deterministic or probalistic (stochastic), algebraic, differential or of any other form for which mathematics provides, a few of which forms will be dealt with in this book. However, they should all satisfy the following prerequisites (BATSCHELET, 1966; KOWAL, 1971):

1. Reasonable simplicity and logical consistency.

2. Mathematical correctness, with perhaps some exceptions, if No. 4 is satisfied.

3. Naturalness with which mathematics represents reality. A model must be rejected if its implications cannot be supported throughout by the events observed or measured. Some deviations may be acceptable if they appear to be due to oversimplification or to influences not covered by the model.

4. Ability to generate predictions.

5. Comprehensiveness, e.g. a model should be applicable to a class of phenomena, not to a single event only.

6. Consistency with physical science.

According to BATSCHELET (1966) the models proposed by Darwin and Mendel satisfy all these requirements. There are, however, many more models which fail to comply in one or other respect. Often it is not known whether they are consistent with physical models. As long as they do not obviously violate them they may, however, still be acceptable. Lack of comprehensiveness is the shortcoming most often encountered in biology. A satisfactory experimental verification of a mathematical model is essential as the only permissible way to draw any conclusion from it. For model builders who follow these rules, the key to effective modeling lies in striking "... an appropriate balance between realism and abstraction for the purpose in hand" (PATTEN, 1971). And if they do not succeed straightaway it is comforting that "... even a bad model may be useful in providing some kind of intellectual foothold in a new and difficult problem" (HARRIS, 1960).

If we ask what kind of mathematics is or will be utilized in epidemiology we may distinguish with BATSCHELET (1966) at least four different levels:

1. Mathematical symbols are used for some models. This comprises mostly elementary mathematics. An example is VAN DER PLANK's (1963) threshold theorem $iR > 1$.

2. Elementary or advanced mathematics (including stochastic processes) are used for models to be applied to concrete situations, the most frequent case in epidemiology.

The important role statistical methods play in epidemiology is detailed in the next two points.

3. Descriptive statistical and graphical methods can, even without a model, be used to reduce the vast amount of data to the essential information it contains. This comprises means, standard deviations and similar statistica, curves, lines, histogram etc. Often diagrams as schematics of interdependence etc. may reveal sufficiently how systems can be subdivided or which parameters or variables may be

eliminated from the model without loss. This may not be so evident from equations (WESTCOTT, 1960). They are universal in application and not peculiar to epidemiology. Reference to statistical textbooks and MOGK (p. 55) must suffice here.

4. Hypotheses can be tested by means of statistical methods, based on appropriately planned experiments, definitely linking empirical facts derived from biological objects.

A well-organized mathematical model may become a genuine research tool, though the precision and simplicity of mathematical physics will be rare in epidemiology. Deductions from theory may lead to ignored or unexpected conclusions that could be tested experimentally. One may also regard it as a tool for decision-making, contributing (indirectly) to breaking down mental barriers, and stimulating creativity (BATSCHELET, 1966). Though many of them are to be solved by numerical approximation or probabilities on digital computers, mathematical models do not always lead to calculation of numbers. Very often they only establish relations between magnitudes. Logics also plays an important role in mathematical modeling, particularly in simulators.

Amongst other applications, mathematical models are essential in the study of epidemics for the analysis of effects and structures. As a quantitative science, epidemiology has to analyse the relevance of variables lending themselves to quantitative measurements and to disentangle all their complex effects on the two interlocking populations, host and pathogen which then yield a third population, lesions. Mathematics in this context not only provides for a precise formulation of basic assumptions and statements, but also for instrumental equations which actually make analyses possible. We shall go into some detail when reviewing and discussing the role and scope of mathematical analysis in epidemiology (p. 7 to 54), setting the framework for the four more detailed and specific papers to follow. This first paper will also deal with some other areas of applied mathematics that seem to have potential use in epidemiology.

Complexity in epidemics stems from the great number and different types of variables (ecological, genetic, endogenous, exogenous to the population, etc.) the different levels of organization (host, pathogen, disease), "and nonhomogeneous and nonuniform distribution of entities in space and time" (WATT, 1966). Because of this complexity a large number of incidences of relevant disease—host—environment—control constellations have to be measured and analyzed. All this invariably brings about a mass of confused data (MOGK, p. 61 to 63). It also immediately leads to a multivariate situation with several independent variables and one or more dependent variables such as disease progress curves. The latter describe the epidemic, and summarize the effects. BUTT and ROYLE (p. 78 to 114), JOWETT et al. (pp. 115, 116) and also WAGGONER (pp. 138, 139) discuss problems and implications of these statistical methods. It becomes obvious that it will not be enough just to adopt regression, correlation, variance and co-variance analyses, be it uni- or multivariate, to analyze data in epidemiology. Much research is still required to develop more, better and meaningful analytical methods in epidemiology.

Computers have meanwhile become an indispensable tool of epidemiological experimentation. The computer also makes possible computional operations which we shall have to face in epidemiology. For this reason MOGK (p. 55 to 77) reviews the use of the computer as an essential research tool in epidemiology.

When chance fluctuations are essential factors, as in disease dissemination, or growth rates, as in disease progress curves, quite advanced mathematics is called for. In the case of the deterministic approach, which still prevails in the epidemiology of plant diseases, differential, integral or similar equations rank high. JOWETT et al. (p. 115 to 136), therefore, give ample attention to this group of mathematical models, particularly growth functions. Some remarks on the hitherto neglected stochastic methods will be found on pages 47 to 50.

As in epidemics, models will become increasingly complicated and sophisticated and a closed mathematical form may no longer be sufficient for them. "Here computer simulation is unavoidable" (BATSCHELET, 1966). Computer simulation may be advisable for two reasons (apart from other benefits): 1) when too many experiments would be needed for a satisfactory explanation of elements and structures of an epidemic, than time and financial resources would permit, and 2) when experiments may not be feasible because of high and costly risks. Computer programs are very flexible and potent tools which enable us to experiment with epidemics indoors in the computer center. This is WAGGONER's (p. 137) subject, to whom we may here refer for details, as well as to JOWETT et al. (p. 129) for some additional facets.

After having read the following 5 chapters the reader may feel that epidemiology, as far as its mathematical models and tools are concerned, is still in its early stages. This is certainly true for three reasons mainly: (1) the time-lag due to its being a young science, (2) the fact that too few plant pathologists have as yet devoted themselves to this branch of plant pathology and (3) that also too few mathematicians have shown interest in this aspect of biomathematics. There is, however, no reason to be discouraged in view of its incipient development. This should rather be a challenge to generations of young plant pathologists—there is still ample scope for pioneer work.

References

BAKER, R.: The dynamics of inoculum. In: Ecology of soil pathogens (ed. K. F. BAKER, W. C. SNYDER) pp. 395–409. London: John Murrey 1965.

BATSCHELET, E.: The application of mathematics to biological problems. Bioscience **16**, 22–24 (1966).

COHEN, Y., ROTEM, J.: Field and growth chamber approach to epidemiology of *Pseudoperonospora cubensis* on cucumbers. Phytopathology **61**, 736–737 (1971).

EDWARDS, A. W. F.: Models in genetics. In: Models and analogs in biology (ed. J. W. L. BEAMENT) pp. 6–12. Cambridge: Univ. Press 1960.

GARRETT, S. O.: Inoculum potential. In: Plant pathology. An advanced treatize (ed. J. G. HORSFALL, A. E. DIMOND) Vol. III, pp. 23–56. New York and London: Academic Press 1960.

HARRIS, J. E.: A review of the symposium. In: Models and analogs in biology (ed. J. W. L. BEAMENT) pp. 250–255. Cambridge: Univ. Press 1960.

KACSER, H.: Kinetic models of development and heredity. In: Models and analogs in biology (ed. J. W. L. BEAMENT) pp. 13–27. Cambridge: Univ. Press 1960.

KOWAL, N. E.: A rationale for modeling dynamic ecological systems. In: Systems analysis and simulation in ecology (ed. B. C. PATTEN) pp. 123–194. New York and London: Academic Press 1971.

KRANZ, J.: Epidemiology, concepts and scope. In: Current trends in plant pathology (ed. S.P. RAYCHAUDHURI, J.P. VERMA) pp. 26–32. Lucknow: Univ. of Lucknow 1973.

MOTT, D.G.: The analysis of determination in population systems. In: Systems analysis (ed. K.E.F. WATT) pp. 179–194. New York and London: Academic Press 1966.

PATTEN, B.C.: Introduction to modeling. In: Systems analysis and simulation in ecology (ed. B.C. PATTEN) Vol. I, pp. 3–121. New York and London: Academic Press 1971.

VAN DER PLANK, J.E.: Plant diseases: epidemics and control. New York and London: Academic Press 1963.

WAGGONER, P.E., HORSFALL, J.G.: EPIDEM—a simulator of plant disease written for a computer. Bull. Connecticut Agric. Expt. Stat. No. 698, 1969.

WATT, K.E.F.: The nature of systems analysis. In: Systems analysis in ecology (ed. K. E. F. WATT) pp. 1–14. New York and London: Academic Press 1966.

WESTCOTT, J.E.: Estimation of values of parameters of a model to conform with observations. In: Models and analogs in biology (ed. J.W.L. BEAMENT) pp. 102–139. Cambridge: Univ. Press 1960.

CHAPTER I

The Role and Scope of Mathematical Analysis and Modeling in Epidemiology

J. KRANZ

1. Introductory Remarks

If we accept that epidemiology deals with two or even three populations, namely: host, pathogen and diseases, and effects upon them, we also have to agree with the following facts:

a) All these populations are characterized by a number of elements and structures (Figs. 1 and 2). They obey mathematical principles, and are best described and explained by mathematical models. Models and mathematical methods are the tools for elucidating elements, structures, and effects of the three populations in-

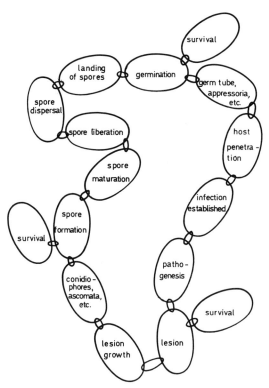

Fig. 1. A schematic of an infection chain (GÄUMANN, 1951) for one pathogen generation (cycle). Each of the "links" is an element of the epidemic

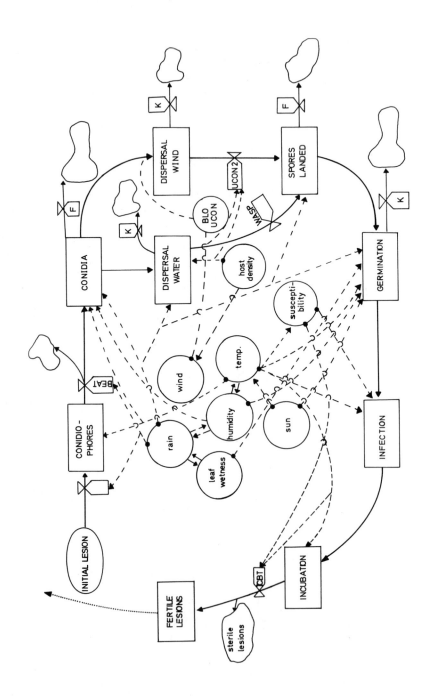

Fig. 2. The structure of the simulator EPIVEN for apple scab (from KRANZ et al., 1973) showing interactions of elements during one pathogen generation

volved in epidemics, whilst conducting experiments and research projects which penetrate into the unknown or close gaps in our knowledge.

b) We are also aware that quantitative measurements on these elements and structures, as well as the effects of environmental factors and human interference upon them, yield vast and complex data, sometimes with large variability. To disentangle, reduce and analyse these data, and consequently the structures and effects, we again need mathematical methods, including statistics, models and computer technology. When trying to subject epidemics to mathematical analysis we must often "employ concepts which merge a great many factors into one measurable whole" (MUENCH, 1959), but for a proper interpretation of the results, the nature of the disease in question must be well known.

Mathematical modeling is largely based on what mathematicians call approximation of mathematical functions, models etc. to empirical phenomena and experimental results (JOWETT, p. 117). Experimental data used for modeling may either be "alien" or specific. "Alien data" are data obtained from experiments or observations which were meant to answer some other question. Or they are data which have accumulated in the literature, while the model was only conceived at a later date by someone else. VAN DER PLANK'S (1963) book is such a fruitful accomplishment. Specific in this context are data which the experimenter himself tries to approximate by means of linear regressions, or any other function, for their evaluation. This is widely made use of and Tables 4–8 present some examples. A typical example for the former is SCHRÖDTER'S (1965) treatment of COHEN and YARWOOD'S (1952) experimental data on growth curves of some hundred fungi. He looked for a function which describes as closely as possible those curves relating growth to temperature. A trigonometric polynomial gave the best fit and was named "temperature equivalence" by SCHRÖDTER.

This is

$$Y = \sin^2(a_1 x + a_2 x^2 + a_3 x^3) \tag{1}$$

with the determining equation

$$Y = \sin^2(1.28x - 0.00746x^2 + 0.00127x^3)$$

for the general form of the temperature curve. For the special temperature equivalent x is

$$x = \frac{t - t_n}{t_x - t_n} \cdot 100 \tag{2}$$

where: t = actual temperature, t_n = minimum temperature and t_x = maximum temperature.

ANALYTIS (1973) used this function for apple scab (Fig. 3), we (KRANZ et al., 1973) have incorporated it into a number of the variables of our simulators, and DIRKS and ROMIG (1970) (the latter, however, with different constants), as well as BURLEIGH et al. (1972), also found this function useful. An apparently versatile mathematical model has thus emerged from approximation.

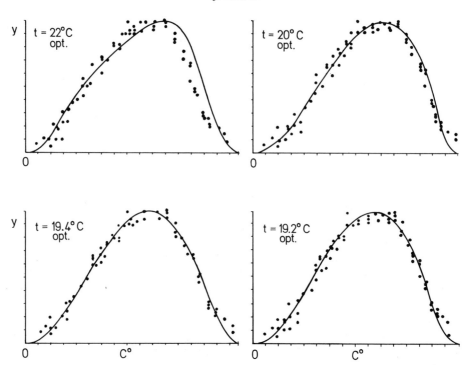

Fig. 3. The iterative process of approximating laboratory measurements on germination of *Venturia inaequalis* to Schrödter's temperature equivalence (from ANALYTIS, 1973, Fig. 1)

A variety of mathematical models were adopted from meteorology for epidemiology in a similar fashion, as for instance, for the air-borne dispersal of propagules. Comprehensive accounts of this legacy have been presented by SCHRÖDTER (1960) and GREGORY (1972) (p. 33). Models for deposition gradients (p. 134) are based on Stoke's law and Sutton's equations, estimation of distance of spore dispersal (p. 36) on Rombakis' model. Stoke's law also appears in Buller's sporobola $D = H/(2a^2/9\mu)$ (INGOLD, 1960), an equation which describes the distance of horizontal throw of released spores, and an equation of velocity of the fall of ellipsoid spores. Perhaps the best known examples of approximation by plant pathologists are Van der Plank's fundamental models published in his books (1963, 1968), and other contributions (1960, 1967). There is no doubt that the influence on epidemiology during the past decade of the logarithmic, apparent and basic infection rates and all concepts based upon them (p. 30 and JOWETT et al.), has been important. They have given this science the long-needed theoretical framework, base, and at the same time a great boost.

Approximation uses available evidence, often comparative. Modeling in this way exemplifies how to extract from experimental information models, often simple and lucid which spark off new ideas, and are useful research tools. For example Schrödter's temperature equivalence allows an analysis of the function of temperature on various elements of fungal life. GREGORY (1968, 1972) has shown how distance and kind of spore sources can be evaluated by means of his models. Flight distance, duration etc. of air-borne spores can be calculated stochastically with a few meteorological and spore parameters using SCHRÖDTER'S (1960) equations. Van der Plank has also provided us with an arsenal that helps to analyse the effects of latent periods, infectious periods, inoculum before onset of epidemics, density of hosts, plot size etc., and also the effects of control measures such as sanitation, resistance and fungicides on the initial inoculum y_0, and the apparent infection rate r.

Our subject being a sketch of the role and means of mathematical analysis of epidemics we cannot treat it, without reviewing briefly how the data to be analysed are obtained. It will become obvious that this aspect of epidemiology may already require mathematics and suitable models. Section 2 therefore treats measurement of host—pathogen—environmental and control factors and their effects. But in subsequent attempts to analyse these data, the role of mathematical analysis and models in epidemiology will be:

— Analysis of population parameters, and effects (Section 3)
— Analysis of changes in populations (Section 4)
— Prediction of epidemic events and control measures required (Section 5)
— Classification (Section 6).

We conclude with some final remarks on stochastic methods in epidemiology (Section 7).

2. Measurement in Epidemiology

Measuring plant diseases and their determining factors is the domain of *quantitative epidemiology*. This usage of the term deviates perhaps from that of other authors. But as epidemiology is chiefly an *a priori* quantitative science, we feel the above term should be restricted to this particular meaning.

We do not wish to be too elaborate here. A few suggestions and remarks together with further references must suffice in the context of this book. See also Mogk's Section 2.

2.1 What Kind of Experiments?

There are hardly any epidemics in the laboratory. There may be epidemics in greenhouses but in the field they certainly occur. Consequently epidemiological experiments have in the first instance to be conducted in the field, at least temporarily. This invariably means numerous variables to be measured and analyzed; variables which not only influence the epidemic but also interact amongst themselves. The knowledge of these interactions however, is essential for the understanding of epidemics. Their measurement is meaningful only when done in the field. Conventional laboratory methods can easily be misleading. Conventional lay-outs of field trials may also have limited scope for quite a few projects. Often "holistic" field trials will be more suitable (KRANZ, 1972). These deviate in some respects from the "randomized block", "latin square", etc. (KRANZ, 1972):

a) Numerous variables derived from pathogen, host environment, and control measures, are measured frequently, often in different ways and sometimes with great exactitude, whenever accessible or considered pertinent. Feasibility, however, compels the choice of those variables, which on the basis of available information

seem to have a great effect. On the other hand many relevant factor constellations for comprehensive tests of their interactions with the disease will often be required.
b) This requires a more or less extensive use (temporarily or permanently) of apparatusses or field laboratories, as in experimental ecology or meteorology.
c) It also requires automatic data processing exceeding purely statistical computations because of the large and complex body of data that emerge from these experiments.

Trials of this kind imply random numbers, replications (which may even follow randomized blocks, factorial experiments etc.) and a statistically adequate sample size. But in comparison to the standard lay-outs they produce two additional sources of errors: 1. inherent differences between experimental units (leaves of the host, lesion of the pathogen, temperature, criterion for the action of fungicide, to quote some examples), and 2. lack of uniformity in experimental techniques and procedures.

Errors of the first kind cannot be entirely avoided, though an appropriate choice of variables and sufficient replication may help to minimize them. Possible errors of this nature have to be taken into account when evaluating the results. Lack of uniformity in methods is a shortcoming which only improved techniques and adequate equipment can overcome. Both sources of errors demand imagination, thorough knowledge and the ability to use methods, equipment and exact planning, as well as discipline and observations during the experiments. Planning also has to take into account the requirements of subsequent computerized evaluation of data (MOGK, p. 59). For further details on this see KRANZ (1972), ANALYTIS (1973) and PLATT and GRIFFITHS (1969) for some rules and axioms (pp. 53–55). Pilot tests are often indispensable to decide which phenometric, bioclimatological etc. variables are possibly to be considered, with what accuracy, methods or equipment, and sample size.

Holistic field experiments, however, only allow for measurements *in situ* of the factors regulating an epidemic. They may yield models for disease forecasters (p. 39), but they hardly permit a straightforward causal analysis, at least not always. Sophisticated growth chambers or phytotrons are needed to check the causal relevance of variables, or whole models, filtered by these experiments and the subsequent analyses. Traditional laboratory experiments may now be recommended for specific clarifications. There will also be an array of experiments (emanating from systems analysis in particular), which have not yet been conceived or have been found trivial until now (e.g. how many sporophores are formed per mm^2 of lesion, how often each of them sporulates etc.).

The schematic in Fig. 4 depicts the procedure just described in the form of a flow chart.

2.2 Measurement of the Host Population

In principle, methods of measurement used in ecology apply (GREIG-SMITH, 1964; KAY, 1966; EVANS, 1972).

There may, however, be differences in interpretation of which the two most important specific aspects should be pointed out. These are host resistance, on both the individual and population level, and its ontogenetic changes. Criteria for these

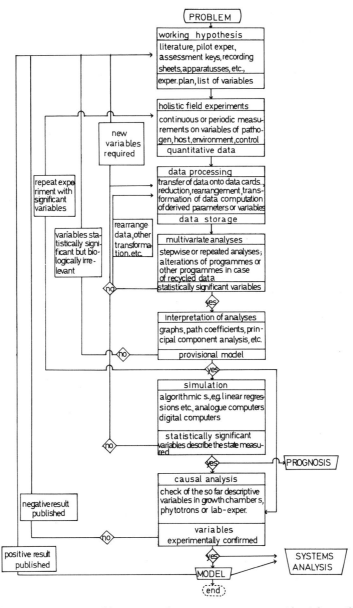

Fig. 4. A flowchart showing a possible course of experimentation in epidemiology (from KRANZ, 1972)

measurements have to be developed by the plant pathologist. As far as plant surfaces are concerned, the epidemiologist has two views: in connection with increase in disease (e.g. populations of lesions) only the amount of *susceptible* host tissue is important at any given time. Microclimate, spread of propagules etc., however, are affected by the whole of the plant surface of a host population. In this aspect the epidemiologist must also to some extent depend on his own criteria (ZADOKS, 1961, 1972). For the calculation of leaf surfaces a number of instrumental equations have been suggested (ANALYTIS et al., 1971).

When measuring quantitative and phenological changes of the host we have always chosen to mark the respective host organs. This permitted us to use the same units throughout one vegetation period, and thus reduce variability. Phenological changes have been expressed according to existing botanical keys, where each stage is considered as a class in quantitative terms. The same can be applied to shades of color of leaves, etc. Time intervals of measurements are largely dictated by the growth rate and precision required.

2.3 Measurement of Populations of Pathogens

Plant pathogens are microorganisms, preponderably fungi. The majority of them live within their host's tissues. An important exception are the powdery and the black mildews (Erysiphales and Meliolales), which are ectoparasites. What we can see on the host surfaces are lesions and sometimes their propagules. To estimate or measure a pathogen's population, therefore, one has to depend on lesions (see 2.4.) and/or on spores, either on lesions or air-borne (JOWETT et al., p. 122).

A pathogen's population may be measured because of the possible damage it may cause to the crop. Here the population of lesions (see below) will ensure an adequate estimate. The other aspect is propagation of disease. A population of lesions may be misleading unless one can distinguish lesions that have passed the latent period and are actually in their infectious period i on which VAN DER PLANK (1963) bases the basic infection rate R. Only infectious tissue forms and releases spores. The amount of infectious tissue can be estimated from samples, provided that a preceding study has established the sporulation intensity in relation to the age or color of lesions sampled, as shown by KRANZ (1968) for the Sigatoka disease of bananas. The surface of infectious lesions may also be computed by means of appropriate equations (ellipse etc.). Sometimes precautions must be taken to differentiate between pathogenic and apathogenic parts of the pathogen population as in the same lesion. Coffee berry disease is a case in point (GIBBS, 1969; VERMEULEN, 1970).

Populations of pathogens can be sampled more directly by spore traps of various devices (MAY, 1967; GREGORY, 1972, for discussion, HIRST et al., 1967). Volumetric spore traps have gained some importance, because they allow quantitative, time-related measurements. Though fairly efficient some vagaries often exist as for the interpretation of the measurements and detection thresholds. The relation between spore catches and disease around the spore trap is not always as reliable as in the case of JOWETT et al. (p.124) or KERR and SHANMUGANATHAN (1966), (Table 4). MALOY and ALEXANDER (1958) have employed the method of the "most probable number" for an estimation of populations of parasitic soil fungi, which could be a promising approach. In the computer age, all spore catches should preferably be on an hourly basis.

We have few simple and elegant methods to measure viability, together with aggressiveness and virulence (VAN DER PLANK, 1968) of the spores caught. Sampling from sticky surfaces is possible but very often time-consuming. Very simple though flexible mathematics have been suggested to designate races of a pathogen and its virulence (HABGOOD, 1970). A binary code for the designation of an isolate according to its virulence on differential varieties may run as follows $2^4 + 2^2 + 2^1 = 16 + 4 + 2 =$ race 22. Its virulence may be coded as 0110100 (when using seven "differentials").

2.4 Measurement of Disease

Disease for an epidemiologist is primarily a population of lesions caused by a given pathogen. These lesions may be leaf spots, blights, anthracnoses, rust pustules, areas continuously covered by powdery mildew, a wilting plant, or any other symptom. It has to be defined specifically in every case. A population of lesions grows in two ways: Individual lesions increase in size, sometimes as long as host tissue is available. But as an infectious lesion may give rise to daughter lesions, the number of lesions consequently increases in time and, simultaneously, in space. VAN DER PLANK (1963) has gone into some detail on both aspects, to which we may refer. Our subject is how to measure disease, the intensity of which we call y, because it is usually read on the ordinate. For a general treatment of measurement of disease see LARGE (1966).

2.4.1 **The Criteria for Measurement.** Disease should always be measured or estimated in quantitative terms. Indexes should also be avoided because they tend to yield somewhat opaque figures. The intensity y of a disease may either be *disease frequency,* e.g. the number of diseased host plants (or organs) in 100 plants counted irrespective of the severity on each of them (or with a threshold), or *disease severity,* e.g. the proportion of the diseased (and generally the susceptible) host surface. Both values are either expressed as 0–100%, or 0 to 1.

A special case is *the number of new infections* (ANALYTIS, 1973; MOGK, 1973; STEINER, 1973) for diseases with distinct symptoms, such as spots.

Measurements should be in appropriate intervals, which are mostly governed by the frequency of favorable infection periods and/or the duration of incubation periods. Weekly, fortnightly or, in some cases, monthly intervals have become customary.

2.4.2 **How to Measure Disease.** Counting of disease frequency and new infections is accurate and simple as long as the plots are small and/or the diseased plants accessible. Beyond this only estimates are feasible. (ANALYTIS and KRANZ, 1972). Their rating should follow established keys which are based on an appropriate transformation of the disease progress curve (either ideal or actual). The range (0,1) or (0–100%) should be divided into classes in such a way that the physiology of the human eye is taken into account (Weber–Fechner law) and errors of estimates are minimized. Keys of this nature have been proposed for logarithmic transformation (HORSFALL and BARRATT, 1945; KRANZ, 1970; ANALYTIS, 1973a) logits (KRANZ, 1970), and for $S_k = a \cdot (q^k - 1)/(q - 1)$, the generalized term of a geometric sequence (ANALYTIS, 1973a). Both the transformation model as well as the lowest class limit (e.g. 0.1 or 1% disease) influence upper and lower limits of subsequent classes and their means (KRANZ, 1970a). Obviously 4 to 7 classes, plus the 0-class, seem to suffice, depending on the issue (KRANZ, 1970).

Estimates, even with keys, can be cumbersome or subject to undesirable variations. More practical techniques are being sought. One is the estimation of the disease y by means of infrared aerial photography which is already quite advanced for some few diseases. Spore catches which correlate highly with y give another promising line to follow. A good example is that of KERR and RODRIGO (1967) which proves that incidence of blister blight of tea can be predicted from spore catches 3 weeks in advance (Table 4) and JOWETT et al. (p. 124). In view of replacing estimates by the more accurate method of counting, ANALYTIS and KRANZ (1972) have investigated the question of a correlation between disease frequency and severity of two diseases. One of them had a curvilinear disease frequency vz. a linear disease severity curve, whereas with the other both curves were linear. They suggested that after transformation in both cases equivalence could be ensured by means of a lag-correlation.

2.4.3 On Sample Sizes. Normally plant diseases are not evenly distributed in their host populations. Large spatial variation is the rule as long as epidemics are in their logarithmic or exponential stages. Disease frequency of some diseases may be near unity in later stages, but disease severity can then still show an uneven pattern. Consequently, the question of adequate sample size coping with the variability in disease arises. Little has been done on this so far, though there exist quite a few books on sampling and sample size for censuses, and similar (HANSEN et al., 1953; COCHRAN, 1963; YATES, 1971).

Following COCHRAN (1963), ANALYTIS and KRANZ (1972) have shown how to calculate an optimal sample size for apple scab in two stages (e.g. branches and leaves as sampling units).

Their models consider both the anticipated precision of measurement and costs involved in sampling. The latter is essential as it is not always feasible to work with sample sizes based on variability alone. They found that

$$m_{opt} = \frac{S_w}{S_u} \cdot \sqrt{\frac{C_u}{C_e}} \tag{3}$$

and

$$n_{opt} = 1/V(y) \cdot \left(S_u^2 + \frac{S_w^2}{m_{opt}} \right) \tag{4}$$

or, in case of a fixed precision the equation becomes

$$n_{opt} = 1/2 + m_{opt} \cdot (C_u n + C_e nm) \tag{5}$$

where n = the number of branches, m = number of leaves, $V(y)$ = Variance of the mean, S_u^2 and S_w^2 from a two-way analysis of variance, C_u and C_e = time needed to rate branches and leaves, respectively. This has been extended also to a sampling in three stages (trees, branches, leaves, ANALYTIS and KRANZ, 1972).

The above model is based on information which must be known beforehand. It also transpired that these equations can only help to reduce sample size when the

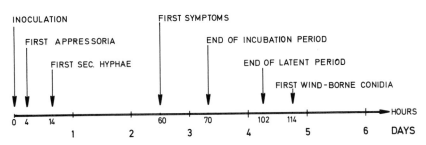

Fig. 5. Infection and disease development of *Erysiphe graminis* f. sp. *hordei* at 22° C, 70 r. h., 18 000 lux, 12 hrs light/dark periods (from Aust, 1973)

original sample size was too large. The determination of sample size in advance proved impossible. The possibility cannot be excluded that all models suggested for censuses work in this way.

2.5 Measurement of Environmental Factors

Here again the plant pathologist has to rely on standard methods to measure meteorological, soil, or other factors (GEIGER, 1961; STEUBING, 1965; WADSWORTH, 1968; PLATT and GRIFFITHS, 1969). In only a few instances can one perhaps take some liberties when employing one's own devices. There are, however, some weather factors which are more important in epidemiology than normally in meteorology, such as leaf wetness and dew, precipitation per hour, droplet size, eddies and wind gust, to quote but a few.

One of the most critical elements of epidemics is the process leading to infection, which in most cases is completed within a few hours (Fig. 5). Incubation and latent periods may also be expressed in hours though there are pathogens that need weeks, months or years. All climatological measurements should therefore be recorded on an hourly basis. The computer can easily rearrange and derive data (hours of leaf wetness, hours of leaf wetness and a temperature from 15–20° C etc.) from such information.

Though precise microclimatological measurements are desirable for the explanation of causal relationships, forecasting, and simulation, data from the weather hut have often proved to be satisfactory.

2.6 Measurement of the Efficiency of Control Measures

VAN DER PLANK (1963, 1967, 1968) has offered models which proved to be instrumental for the explanation of the effects of vertical and horizontal resistance, protective fungicides and adverse weather conditions on disease progress. However, measurement itself is achieved either by measuring disease (2.4.2 and 5.2) or specific experimental techniques, mostly comparing spore germination, sporulation intensity, infection levels, or similar.

3. Analysis of Population Parameters and Effects

By effects we here mean the action of independent variables on the elements of epidemics and their structures. These effects are eventually expressed in some dependent variables, such as the disease progress curve. For their analysis statistical methods are important, but not exclusive.

3.1 Data Reduction

This is certainly the simplest application of mathematical methods in epidemiology. Everybody knows means, standard deviations etc. For details, applications, limitations, and techniques the reader may consult statistical text and source books, as they also apply without being peculiar to epidemiology (MOGK, p. 63). Models are usually not required for these operations, though it may be that models emerge from the results.

A few remarks on plotting of disease progress curves. Whatever the criterion of disease measurements (2.4.1.), two kinds of curves describe the course of an epidemic in time: cumulative and frequency curves. Both can be deduced from each other. Cumulative curves sum up the disease progress over a period of time. They are most commonly employed and describe y at all dates t_i. Ideally sigmoid, one may distinguish a logarithmic, exponential and a transitional slope, and the asymptote or plateau (BAKER, 1971; KRANZ, 1974). A frequency curve relates the increments of disease (over the last measurement) more directly to changes in resistance, environment, control etc. It also shows more clearly the underlying distribution, the skewness and thus the required transformation. Rates of change may be expressed by r (VAN DER PLANK, 1960, 1963, 1967, 1968; KIYOSAWA, 1972a), BS' (ANALYTIS, 1973) and the regression coefficient b. Gradients express the change of pathogens or disease in space from a source (GREGORY, 1968, 1972).

Graphical data reduction can be most helpful. In many cases histograms, curves, lines, Venn diagrams (from set theory) or other forms of pictorial data reduction can be more revealing than statisticas. Before going deeper into statistical analyses experienced epidemiologists cover sheets of paper with sketches to find clues to adequate statistical methods unless it is obvious from the statisticas or dictated by the experimental design. Grid papers are extremely useful in this context.

3.2 Tests of Hypotheses and Models

Tests of significance are also quite familiar. However, it is frequently forgotten that there is a hypothesis—with other words: a model—against which the experimental results are tested by means of a probability function. These functions indicate to what extent the results and the underlying hypothesis can be accepted, and ideally, generalized.

We can also be brief on this subject as it is covered by the statistical literature available to the reader (MOGK, p. 65). The choice of a test (t, χ^2, F, etc.) depends on the kind of test (test of significance, test of parameters, goodness of fit, etc.) and rigidity required. But the underlying distribution, degrees of freedom or some other requirement may also have an influence.

For data reduction and test of hypotheses, computers and statistical library programs may be used, if large bodies of data are to be handled. Usually it is more convenient to solve these numerical problems with modern electronic table computers, either button or program operated.

3.3 Estimation of Parameters

The word parameter is differently used in mathematics. We shall use it in this context in a sense that a parameter is a characteristic of the (host, pathogen and/or disease) population, environment (temperature etc.) and control (dose etc.). Parameters usually have parameter values but there may also be qualitative ones (e.g. "polycyclic" disease). An equation is also said to be in a parametric form, e.g. when written as $x = f(t)$. With estimation of parameters we have in mind the mutual process of experiments and mathematical analyses to determine these parameters and their parameter values from samples taken from the populations. A simple example would be the determination of the a, b_1, b_2, b_3 in $y = a + b_1 x_1 + b_2 x_2 + b_3 x_3$ so that it may read $y = 25.134 + 0.637 x_1 + 0.048 x_2 + 0.007 x_3$. Parameters are treated again by JOWETT et al.

WESTCOTT (1960) distinguishes two approaches to parameter estimation: (1) A causal relationship is assumed between input and output data which are obscured by the presence of random distribution. This is deterministic and the least square fitting of data is appropriate. (2) It is assumed that stochastic terms have some statistical regularity governed by a fixed set of statistical parameters and probability distributions. Parameters in this case will be statistically fluctuating time series, for instance, and one usually measures only some of the many possibilities. Maximum likelihood estimates are an example.

At present the first of these approaches dominates in epidemiology. When studying epidemics in their natural state, one is faced with a multivariate situation consisting of several independent variables and one or more dependent variables. Most important among the dependent variables are the disease progress curves, curves of daily or annual spore catches etc., which describe the epidemic.

Multivariate and complex situations ask for multivariate statistical methods for analysis (SEAL, 1966). They have only come into epidemiology during the past few years, mostly as regression or correlation analyses. First as partial (SCHRÖDTER and ULLRICH, 1965; KERR et al., 1966, 1967; and others), later as full-scale multivariate analyses using comprehensive computer programs (KRANZ, 1968a, 1968b; DIRKS and ROMIG, 1970; EVERSMEYER and BURLEIGH, 1970; ANALYTIS, 1973; MOGK, 1973; ROYLE, 1973; STEINER, 1973; and others).

We can leave it to Butt and Royle to discuss their merits and shortcomings in detail later (p. 109). Whatever the results of linear regression, variance analyses, or others may be, the effects determined by them only describe the probability of causal relationships within the sets of variables which have been measured. A few variables are usually filtered out and explain for some reason or other the majority of variance. This should not be overlooked or misinterpreted, though DIRKS and ROMIG (1970), EVERSMEYER and BURLEIGH (1970) and ANALYTIS (1973) proceeded this way to achieve simulation, and prediction, respectively.

One of the major shortcomings of linear methods is that very often biological processes are not linear. To deal with nonlinearity is, however, not as simple as with the well established linear methods. For this reason most plant pathologists rather tend to put their experimental data into the Procrustes' bed of linear regression analysis. JOWETT and his colleagues will show that this must not always be so (p. 115).

Statistical methods mainly secure relevance and weight of independent variables as parameters measured in quantitative terms. In epidemics we wish to know other parameters as well: e.g. probabilities, distributions, extremes, limits, thresholds, and, of course, rates of change. Extremes, limits and thresholds should ultimately be defined experimentally though they may be located statistically. Distributions and probabilities can be estimated from experimental data by means of appropriate mathematical models, e.g. normal distribution, Poisson distribution and others, or by the application of the theory of probability.

Rates of change require differential and integral calculus for their estimation. Such growth rates are particularly needed for modeling and analyzing population dynamics. VAN DER PLANK (1960, 1963, 1967, 1968) has introduced differential equations and their derivative (the logistic growth function) into epidemiology.

Differential equations are much more flexible than linear regression equations as they not only express the reaction of a disease to "instantaneous values of stimuli" (CASWELL et al., 1972), but can also take into account the state, and thus the recurrence, which has been determined by the history of the epidemic. This flexibility of differential equations is enhanced when they are incorporated in systems analysis. Other growth functions than the logistic one have been studied by ANALYTIS (1973), and will be discussed at length by JOWETT et al.

Beyond these possibilities on which we have touched here, power, exponential, logarithmic and trigonometric functions, and some others may also be used to estimate parameters. Periodic functions are of some interest in the study of biological rhythms.

Parameters which eventually emerge from these processes are incorporated into new models, improve or reject older ones, or give rise to new hypotheses for entirely unforeseen or unexpected experimental approaches.

Parameter estimation is the *conditio sine qua non* for the elucidation of cause-effect pathways and thus the structure of disease and their epidemics. It is also essential for systems analysis which certainly will prove a most useful tool in analyzing structures of diseases. Here it becomes obvious again that modeling is a cyclic and iterative process where experimentation, analysis, and integration are complementary and in most cases temporary.

4. Analysis of Changes in Populations

Epidemics are dynamic processes in time and space. Consequently description and analysis of their dynamics are of paramount interest in epidemiology. This includes, of course, the forces behind that process which are most commonly measured in disease progress curves, curves of spore catches, and deposition or disease gradients. Here again mathematical analysis and modeling often contribute to the study of epidemic structures, cause-effect pathways, and even to parameter estimation. Before we deal with the temporal and spatial changes in epidemics we have to give attention to distributions and transformations. These are prerequisites for population studies. We shall confine ourselves to changes in the populations of pathogens and lesions.

4.1 Distributions

Entities and events of populations are distributed in time and space, as any frequency table or map will show. It will soon become evident that the normal distribution on which most statistical methods, and the probit, logit and logarithmic transformations are based, is not at all common. Transformation of data will, therefore, frequently be required to establish this statistical prerequisite. On the other hand distribution determines the appropriate transformation model for disease progress curves and gradients. Although this is of great importance in epidemiology little is known about it as yet. It may be true that "... the binomial, Poisson and normal distributions can stand a lot of abuse from natural systems without responding badly;", and that "in practice one or other of the transformations ... will generally reduce infection data to usable form when arithmetical values are inadequate" (BALD, 1970). Nevertheless results presented by ANALYTIS (1973) still show that distribution can have a distinct influence on the efficiency of transformations. And it can be asked, whether or not it would be worthwhile to find the real distribution of disease to achieve the most adequate transformation before starting an analysis. As there are quite a few distribution models one can assume that at least some of them also apply to plant diseases, which would leave us with some choice.

The semilog or multiple infection transformation rests on the assumption that multiple infection follows a Poisson distribution (DIMOND and HORSFALL, 1965). Such an assumption requires in turn a more or less uniformly susceptible host tissue and a potentially independent action of equally aggressive propagules. For the probit transformation the susceptible host tissue must be normally distributed in a host population in accordance with the logarithm of the dosage of the pathogen. A skewed normal distribution however, can easily be transformed into a normal standard distribution (ANALYTIS, 1973). This operation is most probably often required in dealing with disease progress curves, daily or annual curves of spore catches, etc. BALD (1970) found binomial distribution rarely applicable to the measurement of host reactions to soil-borne inoculum. There are reports both in favor of and in conflict with the Poisson distribution. However, very often the conflicting results may be accounted for by insufficient compliance with prerequisites in experiments, e.g. deviation from Poisson distribution. No reports are available on the Neyman distribution and other non-random distributions being tested for epidemiological purposes. To test in turn whether the grouping of diseased plants in a field is at random, VAN DER PLANK (1947) used groups of two adjacent trees ("doublets"), to which all larger groups could be reduced. The probability d that of n plants μ diseased ones are adjacent is

$$d = \frac{1}{n} \mu (\mu - 1) \text{ with } \sqrt{d(1-p)} \tag{6}$$

as standard error where $p = 2/n$. This distribution belongs to the binomial series and approaches with large n the Poisson distribution with $\sqrt{d}$ as standard error of d. Laville and Lossois (1963) successfully used the same model (which Van der Plank (1947) also suggested for groups of any size), to prove that the Bayoud disease of date palms is spread by irrigation water. For another application of the Poisson distribution see p. 35.

4.2 Transformations

Transformation of data is a well known procedure in statistics mainly employed to straighten curves, convert percentages, and so on. Transformation of disease progress curves and other graphs of epidemics is essential also for the analysis of epidemics in its various phases (see Van der Plank, 1960, 1963; Zadoks, 1961; Bald, 1970; Kiyosawa, 1972; Analytis, 1973). All this has been commonly accepted, but evidence is accumulating that there is not only one "right" transformation for disease progress curves, such as the semilog, log-log, probit log or logit, to get a crooked disease progress curve straight. Obviously not every curve is an exponential, power or logistic function, nor does it follow the normal or Poisson distribution. There seems to be quite a diversity which deserves the attention of the epidemiologist. The widely accepted standard normal distribution in many cases also appears to be a rather daring assumption. Consequently, quite a few more mathematical functions and distribution models may be needed in future to achieve better transformations on both biological and mathematical grounds. In plain words: do not apply a transformation model blindly to any disease, check suitability first by verification of the underlying distribution.

Transformation of disease curves and gradients in relation to inoculum density of soil-borne diseases is discussed by Dimond and Horsfall (1965) and Baker (1965, 1971). For the multiple infection or semilogarithmic transformation of the number of diseased plants is

$$X/N = 1 - e^{-x/N} \tag{7}$$

or

$$Y/N = (x/N) - \frac{x^2/N^2}{2!} + \frac{x^3/N^3}{3!}, \ldots, \frac{x^n/N^n}{n!} \tag{8}$$

or for less than 10% of plants diseased, that is, when the inoculum is small,

$$Y/N = x/N \quad \text{or} \quad Y = x. \tag{9}$$

Expressed in logarithmics and x the equations is written

$$x = 2.3 N [\lg N - \lg (N - y)], \tag{10}$$

where x is the number of infections that have taken place, while X/N is the proportion of diseased plants. This relation gives a straight line on semilogarithmic paper, with an ordinate divided logarithmically. For a log-log transformation both axes of the coordinate have to be in logarithmic units. The logarithmic-probability or probit transformation shows the survival (%) in probits being linearly related to the inoculum density when data are plotted on a log-probit grid. DIMOND and HORS-FALL (1965) consider this the more realistic transformation of these three methods, which is

$$\text{probit } Y/N = a\,(\lg x) + b \tag{11}$$

with a as the slope of the dosage-responses curve, and b its position, commonly measured in terms of effective dosage (ED). BAKER (1965, 1971) and SNEH et al. (1966) independently used $\ln 1/(1-y)$, that is VAN DER PLANK'S (1963) version of Gregory's multiple infection transformation.

Log-probit curves, however, do not allow for the evaluation of multiple infections (DIMOND and HORSFALL, 1965), as do semilogarithmic transformations. BALD (1970) proposes a rule of thumb (p. 39) when to use probits vz. multiple infection transformation. "... when probit values plotted against log numbers of propagules fall on a rising curve, use the multiple-infection transformation; when the multiple-infection transformation gives values falling away markedly in the higher ranges, use probits."

For the transformation of disease severity BS, which for apple scab has a skewed distribution (Fig. 6), into a normal distribution (BS') ANALYTIS (1973) suggests

$$(BS') = (BS)^{1-b/2} \tag{12}$$

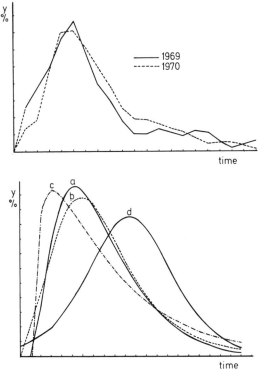

Fig. 6. Frequency curves of apple scab severity in 1969 and 1970 (top) and the curves of the growth functions of (a) Bertalanffy ($n=2$), (b) Gompertz, (c) Mitscherlich ($n=2$), and (d) the logistic function (from ANALYTIS, 1973, Figs. 5 and 6)

Table 1. The effect of transformation on a distribution of estimated disease severity (*BS*) of apple scab. Transformation into *BS'* is achieved by $BS' = BS^{0.23}$, see text (compiled from ANALYTIS, 1973)

No. of class	Limits of classes %	Frequencies of BS	BS'
1	0.1– 3	155	4
2	3.1– 6	37	2
3	6.1– 9	22	13
4	9.1–12	7	23
5	12.1–15	4	31
6	15.1–18	6	48
7	18.1–21	0	39
8	21.1–24	1	34
9	24.1–27	0	22
10	27.1–30	2	13
11	30.1–33	1	3
12	33.1–36[a]	1	4

[a] This was the maximum disease severity observed per leaf.

where *b* is the regression coefficient. In the case of apple scab $b = 1.54$, and

$$(BS') = (BS)^{1-0.77} = (BS)^{0.23} \quad (\text{Table 1}).$$

It is not always linearity that necessitates transformations. The Weber-Fechner-law also demands transformations of estimates to comply with the physiological capability of the human eye (HORSFALL and BARRATT, 1945; KRANZ, 1970; ANALYTIS, 1973a). This is essential for disease assessment keys. Another important application is the trend analysis for all events measured in time, particularly disease progress curves (see also BUTT and ROYLE, pp. 89 to 94). As time has an inherent influence on at least all polycyclic diseases, the time effect has to be eliminated before other effects can be analysed properly. Trend analysis may be achieved by partial regression analysis in case of a linear relationship, and with the Bertalanffy and Mitscherlich growth functions for $n = 2$ (*n* for skewness) in case of curvilinear relationships (ANALYTIS and KRANZ, 1972; ANALYTIS, 1973). Growth functions from which models for transformation of disease progress curves can be derived, by the way, apparently have a wide scope, as shown by ANALYTIS (1973, Tables 2 and 3). For more details on growth functions see JOWETT et al.

4.3 Populations Changing in Time

Time aspects so far have met the greatest interest in epidemiology, as reflected by the published evidence. This mostly refers to the progress of disease, either within a pathogens generation (cycle) or as polycyclic diseases within a vegetation period, year, or any other time unit. We shall return to this in 4.3.4. Let us first, however,

Table 2. Transformation models derived from some growth functions (ANALYTIS, 1973)

Growth function		Equation	Transformation equation
Logistic		$X_i = X_{max}/(1 + be^{-kt})$	$x_i = ln[X_i/(X_{max}/1 - X_i/X_{max})]$
MITSCHERLICH	$n=1$	$X_i = X_{max}(1 - e^{-kt})$	
BERTALANFFY	$n=1$	$X_i = X_{max}(1 - be^{-kt})$	$x_i = ln[1/(1 - X_i/X_{max})]$
MITSCHERLICH	$n=2$	$X_i = X_{max}(1 - e^{-kt})^2$	
BERTALANFFY	$n=2$	$X_i = X_{max}(1 - be^{-kt})^2$	$x_i = ln[1/(1 - \sqrt{X_i/X_{max}})]$
MITSCHERLICH	$n=3$	$X_i = X_{max}(1 - e^{-kt})^3$	
BERTALANFFY	$n=3$	$X_i = X_{max}(1 - be^{-kt})^3$	$x_i = ln[1/(1 - \sqrt[3]{X_i/X_{max}})]$
GOMPERTZ		$X_i = X_{max} \cdot e^{-be^{-kt}}$	$x_i = -ln[-ln(X_i/X_{max})]$

Table 3. Comparison of the efficiency growth functions and some transformations applied to disease progress curves of apple scab (compiled from ANALYTIS, 1973)

Growth function/ transformation		Goodness-of-fit test[a] Probability P %	Coefficient of determination (r^2) for the transformations[b]
No transformation		—	0.84
Logistic/Logits		< 0.1	0.93
Probits		—	0.92
Mitscherlich	$n=1$	0.1	
	$n=3$	>99.0	
	$n=3$	~ 1.0	
Bertalanffy	$n=1$	~99.0	0.99[c]
	$n=2$	>99.0	0.99
	$n=3$	>99.0	0.99
Gompertz		>99.0	0.98

[a] Goodness-of-fit of growth functions to the disease progress curves measured.
[b] For transformation equations see Table 2.
[c] The r^2-values apply for the n of both the monomolecular Mitscherlich and Bertalanffy growth functions.

review some other facets of epidemics which change in time. There are: initial inoculum (4.3.1.), which reflects effects during overwintering and dispersal, and by specific control measures; sporulation and secondary inoculum (4.3.2.) which is a must for the majority of epidemics of plant diseases; and incubation and latent periods (4.3.3.), which by their duration determine the number of pathogen generations during the period a host is susceptible, and largely influence infection rates and ultimate disease incidence. In natural epidemics all of these facets, including disease progress, are strongly dependent on recurrent effects, between as well as amongst themselves. For the solution of problems like this the DO-loop of computer programs is highly suitable, which is another argument in favour of systems analysis.

4.3.1 Initial Inoculum. The amount of inoculum y_0 surviving adverse periods or treatment, and available at the start of a new host crop can have an important bearing on an epidemic. An overwintering rate is suggested for rice blast by KIYO-

Sawa (1972) as $\theta = y_0/yt$. Here is θ = overwintering rate, y_0 = initial number of lesions, yt = number of lesions at the end of the host's vegetation period. The beginning of an epidemic certainly is, and its final severity y_{max}, in many cases seems to be correlated with y_0 (Kranz, 1968 b). Van der Plank's (1963) "sanitation ratio"

$$y/y_s = y_0/y_{0s} \tag{13}$$

takes account of this.

The time needed for a disease to increase from y_s to y (provided the same infection rate r_1 prevails) is the delay Δt

$$\Delta t = 1/r_1 \ln y_0/y_{0s} \quad \text{or} \quad 2.3/r_1 \lg y_0/y_{0s} \tag{14}$$

which is derived from

$$y_0 = y_{0s} e^{r_1 \Delta t} \tag{15}$$

(Van der Plank, 1963) where y_0 = initial inoculum (or disease) with no sanitation, y_{0s} = the amount of disease after sanitation, r_1 = the logarithmic infection rate, and $e = 2.718$.

This delay can, for example, be decisive when yield is correlated with a certain level y of disease at a critical stage of host development; Δt could shift this level beyond that point.

4.3.2 Sporulation and Secondary Inoculum. Sporulation produces inoculum and this in turn disease. Strongly dependent on weather factors, sporulation distinctly fluctuates in time. On top of this there is an overriding influence of time governed by the increase in disease, the rhythm of sporulation during the life time of individual lesions, and the age stratification of the population of lesions. As most of the fungi with their propagules in some way or other become air-borne, sporulation can be measured (2.3) at least in equivalent terms. Based on measurements, some mathematical models have been developed which describe, analyze and/or predict sporulation as it changes with time. We shall present them below in Table 4, and much more is described by Butt and Royle and Jowett et al. on later pages.

4.3.3 Incubation and Latent Period. With each latent period that is passed the pathogen multiplies and fresh inoculum becomes available. Latent periods thus determine spore production and the number of pathogen generation possible. As the length of latent periods varies widely with most diseases, time effects become highly important, particularly for the analysis of this element and for forecasting (Waggoner, 1960; Bourke, 1970). In spite of the great interest that plant pathologists have in predicting this highly variable and crucial element of an epidemic, appropriate and specific research (for which the following models could be guidelines) is still lacking. In Table 5 we list a few models that might well be included here. Another model is Mill's empiric incubation periods for apple scab which have found wide application in disease forecasting (Analytis, 1973).

Table 4. Some proposed equations to estimate change in sporulation[a]

Disease	Host	Equation	Terms	Authors
General		$I = \dfrac{mi\,Q}{x^b} e^{-klc}$	I = Intensity of inoculum, m = a constant, Q = inoculum at the source, c = proportion of propagules able to infect a host, x = distance from source, b = a constant $(0-5)$, e^{-klc} = a term from Beer-Lamberts law of deposition	DIMOND and HORSFALL (1960)
Blister blight	tea	$y = 2.5824 - 0.6169x_1 + 0.06x_2$	y = lg spores per blister, x_1 = lg blisters per 100 shoots, x_2 = mean daily sunshine (h).	KERR and SHANMUGANATHAN (1966)
Stem rust	wheat	$Pi = \dfrac{x_i}{\sum\limits_{i=0}^{n} x_i}$	P_i = Probability of a spore being released on the ith day after inoculation, x_i = number of spores produced on the ith day after inoculation	LEONARD (1969)
		$G = \sum\limits_{i=1}^{n} iP_i$	G = Generation time in n days, P_i as above	
Downy mildew	hop	$y = 0.274 - 0.159x_1 + 0.051x_2 - 0.043x_3$	y = largest hourly spore concentration of a day, x_1 = duration of rainfall (h), x_2 and x_3 = mean temperature (°C)	ROYLE and THOMAS (1972)
Blast	rice	$y = Y/(1 - ke^{-rt})$	y = cumulative spore numbers, Y = maximum for each year, $k = (Y - y_0)/y_0$. y_0 = initial spore numbers.	KIYOSAWA (1972a)

[a] See also JOWETT et al. (p. 120).

VAN DER PLANK (1968) proposes a model for a weighted estimate of the probable duration of the latent period p, either for various portions of a lesion or of various lesions of a population as

$$e^{-pr} = \sum_{j=1}^{n} a_j e^{-p_j r} \tag{16}$$

with $a_1 \ldots a_j \ldots a_n$ as the proportions of the lesion with latent periods $p_1 \ldots p_j \ldots p_n$. Though within experimental reach this model has obviously not yet been adopted for any disease. MOGK (1973) has compared mean, mode and median as measure for the duration of the incubation periods from the positively skewed disease progress curve of the coffee berry disease, of which the mode appeared most satisfactory. Estimation of the incubation period of this disease was also possible from the regression line; also $y_{max}/2$ or the day when 50% of the final disease intensity is reached compares well with the median. These methods require information on rate of increase and final disease incidence prior to calculation.

Also based on experimentation is—as in most known cases—a parabolic function of the incubation period of powdery mildew of barley (AUST and KRANZ, 1974), which is

$$y = 92.97 - 0.0975\, x + 0.00018\, x^2$$

where y = incubation period in hours and x = number of conidia per unit leaf. With this and similar models (Table 5) predictions can be generated provided that the spore catch is known and temperature und host susceptibility remain fairly constant.

4.3.4 The Progress of an Epidemic.
Mathematical modeling of epidemics, or rather its graph, the disease progress curves, practically dates back to VAN DER PLANK'S work (1960, 1963, 1967, 1968). Ever since, new models of various kind (algebraic, differential etc.) have been built in increasing numbers, which are often useful analytical tools for their purposes, and sometimes even beyond. How versatile they can be for the estimation of parameters, structural analysis, and forecasting has been amply demonstrated by Van der Plank. Nevertheless, these models more or less describe input-output relations and largely remain black boxes as far as complex structure gearing the output is concerned. As WAGGONER (p. 142) will show how to disentangle their causal pathways we shall confine ourselves to simple algebraic and differential equations most suitable for describing and analyze changes of the populations in time.

A simple, rather heuristic but fairly early model of an epidemic is that of K. O. MÜLLER (1957) for air-borne diseases

$$D = A(c \cdot P)^{T/t} \tag{17}$$

D = Rate of increase of disease per generation (cycle), A = initial inoculum or disease (y_0), c = number of infectious propagules disseminated per lesion, P = probability of infection (0 = no spore achieves infection, 1 = all spores achieve infection), t = incubation period, T = time.

VAN DER PLANK (1960, 1963) assumes that "at any moment of time, the rate of increase of the total amount of capital plus interest is proportional to the total amount itself at that moment. This is logarithmic increase." However, there is only a "faint analogy" between increase in money and disease. Disease increase differs from growth in interest in four major points: infection is intermittent and not continuous; increase is limited by the host tissue available; there is a delay in sporulation and no immediate reproduction of disease, and diseases occur in foci, the increase of which is less than the logarithmic rate. But Van der Plank remains confident that after appropriate modifications of the principles of logarithmic increase "workable and valid methods of dealing with pathogen populations" could

Table 5. Some proposed equations to estimate infection, incubation and latent periods

Disease	Host	Equation	Terms	Authors
Powdery mildew	barley	$y = 92.97 - 0.0975x + 0.00018x^2$	y = incubation period in hours, x = number of conidia sown on 2 cm^2 of leaf surface	AUST and KRANZ (1974)
Powdery mildew	barley	$y = 2.105 + 0.3816x$	y = number of infection points, x = number of conidia sown on 2 cm^2 of leaf surface	AUST (1973)
Cercospora leaf spot	sugar-beet	$y = 15.444 - 0.53x + 0.056x^2$	y = latent period in days, $x = T - 25$, T = temp. in °C	BLEIHOLDER (1971)
Late blight	potatoes (cv. Erstling)	$\sum_{t \geq 7} (t - 7) = 1543$	degree hours t = temperature in °C above "basic temp." of 7° C	SCHRÖDTER and ULLRICH (1965)
		$y_i = \left[\sum_{k=1}^{3} h_k' F_1(tk) + \sum_{k=4}^{8} h_k' F_2(tk) \right] \times (n - i)_b$	y_i = effect of temperature and humidity or leaf wetness on infection and sporulation, h_k' = frequency of hours with temperatures t_k (modes of 8 classes k each with a range of 2 °C between 8 and 24 °C) other terms, as in Table 7, provided that at least 4 hours of relative humidity $\geq 90\%$ or rain of ≥ 0.1 mm/hour have prevailed. For sporulation $h' \to h''$ = at least 10 hours with the above conditions.	
Downy mildew	hop	$y = 0.037 + 0.023x_1 + 0.066x_2 + 0.02x_3$	y = % leaves infected, x_1 = duration of leaf wetness with a rain contribution, $x_2 = RA$, x_3 = number of spores/m^3 air.	ROYLE (1973)

be developed. No doubt, these four major "points" must challenge plant pathologists to search for models more adapted to the natural course of the particular diseases they study. The compound and simple interest models, on the other hand, seem to fit at least the epidemics of some major diseases, such as late blight of potatoes, cereal rusts and bunt. There is, however, no reason to believe that this is universal. Discontinuous infection models of plant disease cannot be handled as neatly as by some of Van der Plank's continuous models presented below. But VAN DER PLANK (1963) has also proposed a discontinuous infection model which is valid only if p for latent period and t for time are integers, and $np \leq t < (n+1) p$, and $a = R$ then

$$y_t = y_o [1 + a(t - p + 1) + \frac{a^2}{2} (t - 2p + 1)(t - 2p + 2) + \frac{a^3}{3!}$$

$$\cdot (t - 3p + 1)(t - 3p - 2)(t - 3p + 3) \ldots + \frac{a^n}{n!} \tag{18}$$

$$\cdot (t - np + 1)(t - np + 2) \ldots (t - np + n)]$$

The logarithmic increase, as long as there is no limitation to susceptible tissue, is for polycyclic (compound interest) diseases $\frac{dy}{dt} = r_1 y$, and the relative logarithmic infection rate becomes

$$r_1 = (1/t_2 - t_1) \ln (y_2/y_1) \quad \text{or} \quad (2.3/t_2 - t_1) \lg (y_2/y_1) \tag{19}$$

When, however, disease incidence exceeds $y = 0.05$, or for practical purposes $y = 0.35$ $(0 < y \leq 1)$, the healthy proportion of susceptible tissue decreases by $(1 - y)$ and the probability of multiple infection (GREGORY, 1972) increases. To allow for this, Van der Plank replaces the above equation by $dy/dt = ry(1 - y)$, and the relative infection rate

$$r = \frac{1}{t_2 - t_1} \ln \frac{y_2(1 - y_1)}{y_2(1 - y_2)} \quad \text{or} \quad \frac{2.3}{t_2 - t_1} \lg \frac{y_2(1 - y_1)}{y_1(1 - y_2)} \tag{20}$$

the term $\ln y/(1 - y)$ are VAN DER PLANK's (1963) logits and apply to polycyclic diseases. For monocyclic (simple interest) diseases, or the monocyclic phase of polycyclic diseases, $\ln 1/(1 - y)$ is to be used.

The latter is identical to GREGORY's (1972) equation $y = N(1 - e^{x/N})$ for multiple infection transformation multiplied by 100. The terms are: N = number of hosts available, y = average number of hosts infected at random by x parasites.

These equations can be expanded by making allowance for changes in the amount of host tissue h at times 1 and 2 by $m = h_2/h_1$ as

$$\varrho = \frac{1}{t_2 - t_1} \ln \frac{m \cdot y_2}{y_1} \quad \text{or} \quad \frac{2.3}{t_2 - t_1} \lg \frac{m \cdot y_2(1 - y_1)}{y_1(1 - y_2)} \, . \tag{21}$$

Another concept which is offered by VAN DER PLANK (1960, 1963), is the basic infection rate, which is no longer based on the proportion y_t of diseased susceptible host tissue alone, but on that proportion of y which has passed the latent period and thus has become infectious

$$dy_t/dt = R y_{t-p}(1 - y_t) \tag{22}$$

and

$$R = 1/y_0(t_2 - t_1) (\ln 1/1 - y_2 - \ln 1/1 - y_1) \tag{23}$$

where R = basic infection rate, y_0 = initial disease, y_t = disease at time t, and y_{t-p} = proportion of disease that has passed the latent period p.

Taking removals of infectious tissue into account the above equation becomes

$$dy_t/dt = R_c(y_{t-p} - y_{t-i-p})\,(1 - y_t) \tag{24}$$

which by division and rearrangement becomes

$$R_c = ry_t/(y_{t-p} - y_{t-i-p}) \tag{25}$$

R_c = basic infection rate corrected for the proportion of disease that is no longer infectious (removals), y_{t-i-p} = proportion of disease at time t that has passed the latent period p and the infectious period i (removals).

This model measures all four basic processes of an epidemic (VAN DER PLANK, 1968), namely: infection by R, latency by p, abundance of spore production also by R, and all infectious tissue dropping out of spore production (and being removed from the epidemic) by i. The essential difference between both the relative and basic rates are that the latter is founded on the infectious and not on the total diseased host tissue. With the basic infection rate the absolute increase of disease per unit per day is described.

A number of related models and functions have been derived from this one and the r by VAN DER PLANK (1963, 1968). ZADOKS (1971) has used R_c for his simulator (p. 151). We have already indicated that it will not be long before VAN DER PLANK's models, though readily accepted for some epidemics, face the fate of all models: they will be adapted, amended, expanded or replaced by others. Some authors add new parameters or terms, or replace former ones (WAGGONER, 1965; KIYOSAWA, 1972a). Others suggest entirely different models (ANALYTIS, 1973) for the same phenomenon.

KIYOSAWA (1972) proposed a model for disease increase of rice blast which resembles Van der Plank's equation (see above)

$$dy/dt = ry(1 - y/Y)$$

which is solved as

$$y = Y/1 + ke^{-rt} \tag{26}$$

with y = number of lesion (or cumulative spores), Y = maximum lesion (or spore) number in the season, $k = (Y - y_0)/y_0$. In order to avoid any limitations from the amount of host available and to account for an increasing resistance with age the equation is

$$dy/dt = ry(1 - t/T) \quad \text{which is solved as}$$

$$y = y_0 e^{r(t - t^2/2T)} \qquad \text{with } (t \leq T) \tag{27}$$

where t = time and T = time when increase of lesions (or cumulative spores) stops.

WAGGONER (1965) has related the infection rate r to the changing temperature during the season

$$T = T\hat{p} + kt \quad \text{(see below) by}$$

$$r = r_x - b(T - T_x)^2 \tag{28}$$

where r_x = maximum rate attained at the optimum temperature T_x, at $(r_x/b)^{1/2}$-degrees above and below T_x the infection rate is $r = 0$, and then turns negative, which leads to a decrease in disease prevalence. "The parameters r_x, T_x, and b (the regression coefficient) must be estimated after an examination of some essential fungal phase, such as incubation period." Finally Waggoner arrives at

$$\int_{y_0}^{y} \frac{dy}{y} = \int_{0}^{t} [r_x - b(T\hat{p} + kt - T_x)^2] \cdot dt \tag{29}$$

$T\hat{p}$ = temperature at planting time, k = rate of increase in temperature per day during the spring, kt = temperature increase on day t. To take account of rise and fall of temperature during the vegetation period T becomes

$$T = T\hat{m} + A \sin t \tag{30}$$

with $T\hat{m}$ = mean temperature of the year, and A = amplitude or the in temperature from $T\hat{m}$ to summer maximum. Here t = in radians or units of 57 days after 20th April. This leads to

$$\int_{y_0}^{y} \frac{dy}{y} = \int_{0}^{t} [r_x - b(T\hat{m} + A \sin t - T_x)^2] \cdot dt \tag{31}$$

WAGGONER (1965) discusses a number of examples from literature, which fit his model.

Another definition for rates of change in disease severity y taking the asymptote of disease progress curves into account has been formulated by ANALYTIS (1973) as $BS = y$.

$$y = y'_{i+1} - y'_i = \ln 1/(1 - \sqrt{y_{i+1}/y_{max}}) - \ln 1/(1 - \sqrt{y_i/y_{max}}) \tag{32}$$

which, for equidistant intervals of disease readings, is $\cong k$ of the growth rate in the Bertalanffy, Gompertz, and Mitscherlich growth functions. The term y_{max} here stands for maximum disease incidence of the epidemic concerned, or the asymptote.

Based on this, ANALYTIS (1973) has studied a number of symmetric and asymmetric growth functions to describe in mathematical terms disease progress curves (Table 6). Growth rates are dealt with again by JOWETT et al. (p. 125). To verify their suitability for transformation of disease progress curves of apple scab, ANALYTIS (1973) has tested all these growth functions on an analog computer. He found that the logistic function was the least suitable to describe disease progress curves of apple scab. The Gompertz and Bertalanffy functions fitted the observed curves best, the latter irrespective of the skewness ($n = 1$, $n = 2$, $n = 3$). The Mitscherlich function was as effective, but for $n = 2$ only.

4.4 Population Changing in Space

The growth of individual lesions in relation to the growth of a population of lesions has been discussed by VAN DER PLANK (1963). The relative growth rate of a lesion is dependent on its area and thus not logarithmic. However, it is different with populations of lesions: In this case lesions in uniformally susceptible host populations of equal uniformity grow logarithmically as long as there is not too much overlapping of lesions and multiple infections (p. 30) take place. Such a change in space takes a time-span largely determined by the length of the latent period (generations, cycles). But the rapidity by which the pathogen overcomes both the barriers of space and time (WAGGONER, 1962) in a field also affects the distribution of age groups of lesions: A steep increase favors a large proportion of young lesions, an even and constant increase a balanced age grouping, and a slow increase a high share of old sterile lesions. All this affects the ability of a population of lesions to produce propagules, to propagate, and to determine the rate of disease progress.

4.1.1 Gradients.
Gradients may be distinguished as infection (disease) gradient or deposition gradient from a source. Infection gradients are measured in numbers of lesions (2.4) and the deposition gradient by the number of spores caught (2.3). While some evidence (SCHRÖDTER, 1960; GREGORY, 1972) suggests that mathematical models fit observed deposition gradients well, much less is known about infection gradients. For obvious reasons it is in most cases not possible to deduce the latter from the former.

From the various equations published, some selected ones may demonstrate a few principles here:

A deposition coefficient $p = d/n$, where d = number of spores deposited per cm^2 surface, and n = numer of spores suspended per cm^3 of air " ... measures the thickness of the slice of cloud cleared while travelling over unit length of ground surface" (GREGORY, 1972). The same author (1968, 1972) has, amongst other models, proposed a number of mathematical models developed from Sutton's equation to compute the expected depositions gradients at various distances from point, line, strip, and area sources, of which the first and last ones, for example, run

$$D = \frac{p \, 2 \, Q_x}{\sqrt{(\pi)} \, C \, x^{1/2m}} \tag{33}$$

(point source, with *total* number of spores deposited on an annulus 1 cm wide a distance x). WAGGONER (1962) simplifies this equation to $D = (3Q_x)/\sqrt{\pi} \, x)$ by substituting "the reasonable values of 1 and 2 for ... C and m. The x, of course, must be greater than 1"

$$d_{aw} = \frac{p \, 4 \, Q_x}{\sqrt{(\pi)} \, C(2 - m)} \, x^{1 - m/2} \left[\left(1 + \frac{u'}{x} \right)^{-m/2} - 1 \right]. \tag{34}$$

Strip source of width w, d_{aw} the number of spores deposited per cm^2 at a distance x downwind of strip after integration. For the terms in both equations we refer to GREGORY (1972), or to SCHRÖDTER (1960), who also elaborates.

GREGORY (1968) writes that only "a few simple geometrical concepts are essential for interpreting gradients". Modeling here requires a simplification in so far as point or line sources of spores have to be postulated. He distinguishes "6 possibilities" (p. 195), which permit the interpretation of about 400 gradients studied from the literature. Inversely, the gradients of these models allow identification or prediction, whether background source, inactive point source, two localized sources, location of source etc. exist in a particular field. This can be of relevance in spraying trials, determination of cropping distances, field sizes etc. He than points out that practically all infection gradients studied by him can be expressed by the regression coefficient b after adequate, usually log-log transformation.

For an estimate of the danger d_n from air-borne spores which alight from an adjacent field and pass over our field. WAGGONER (1962) has developed a few models, which rest on experimental evidence from late blight of potatoes

$$q = q_0 e^{-(7x^{1/8})/10} \tag{35}$$

where q_0 is the production of spores/cm^2 of source, q = number of spores in the cloud, x = distance. Thus the number of propagules (of *Phytophthora infestans*) arising from the 1 cm strip of the neighboring field is

$$d(x) = (3q_0)/(\pi^{1/2} x \, e^{(7x^{1/8})/10}) \tag{36}$$

with $d(x)$ = number of propagules arriving. In adjacent square fields with sides Δx, with distances x_0 from center to center being considerably greater than Δx, the danger d_n from the neighbor at last becomes

$$d_n = (3q_0/\pi^{1/2})(\Delta x/x_0)^2 [e^{(-7x_0^{1/8})10}/1 + e^{(-7x_0^{1/8} \cdot 2^{1/8})10}/2$$
$$+ e^{(-7x_0^{1/8} \cdot 3^{1/8})}/3 \ldots]. \tag{37}$$

Any danger d_n to a unit area of our field is considered by WAGGONER (1962) as being " ... a function of the distance x_0 between the fields and of the fraction $(\Delta x/x_0)^2$ of the area of the region that is occupied by fields."

The danger of receiving inoculum from one's own field is estimated by the model (WAGGONER, 1962, for details and derivation), given here for a field of 1 hectare as

$$d_0 > 3q_0/\pi^{1/2} \cdot 2.8 . \tag{38}$$

Here we have the interesting case of an inequality, very rare so far in plant pathology.

WAGGONER (1962) suggests probability models to predict mean number of hits of propagules I that will be showered on to a field per cm^2 from a point source of n lesions and the distance x between source and target

$$I = 27 n e^{(-0.7x^{1/8})} x^{-2} \tag{39}$$

and, depending on the preceding model, for the probability $P_{(j)}$ that j spores strike a field

$$P_{(j)} = I^j / e^I j! \tag{40}$$

which is the Poisson distribution with I as before.

Departing from these models, WAGGONER (1962) then discusses and tabulates consequences like: probability $P_{(1/j)}$ that j spores occupy i areas in a field, probability $P_{(i)}$ that i areas in a field are occupied, hazard H of fields by shape and size, consequences $E(i)H$ of inoculum potentials and fields, and the extinction of an invasion. He also gives a table for $P_{(0)}$, $P_{(1)}$, $P_{(5)}$, $P_{(11)}$, and $P_{(20 \text{ to } 40)}$ under the influence of the distance x, number of lesions in the source ($n/1000$), area of the target field (ha) and mean deposition of spores per field (I).

A somewhat similar probability model has been suggested by GARRETT, quoted by BAKER (1971), for soil-borne fungi. It is an equation which departs from the assumption of independent action of propagules (e. g. the regression $x, y = 0$, and y proportional to x within the domain of x) for the probability P that a host will be infected by a density d of spore is

$$P = 1 - (1 - p)^d \tag{41}$$

with p as the probability that any one spore will succeed in infecting. Writing the above equation in terms of p it runs

$$p = 1 - (1 - p)^{1/d} \tag{42}$$

and for the ED_{50} — value of P the equations is

$$p = 1 - 0.5^{1/d}$$

This would permit predicting success (in %) of individual propagules in an infection court when the inoculum density-infection curve is known.

Other entirely different models are by BAKER et al. (1967) who have formulated 4 models of the behavior of soil pathogens in relation to their inoculum density. These are based on combinations of fixed or mobile inoculum, and fixed or mobile infection courts.

In addition BAKER (1971) distinguishes between rhizosphere and rhizoplane influence on inoculum density. The former being a function of pN (N number of propagules in the rhizosphere and the probability p of these infecting) has a slope of 1.00, whereas the latter turns out with a slope of 0.67 on a log-log grid. His tests of these models with empiric data from the literature gave satisfactory corroboration.

4.4.2 The Flight of Air-borne Spores.

It is the flight of air-borne spores that contributes most to the long distance spread, also called epidemic spread (GÄUMANN, 1951). It is known to be governed by meteorological factors and various obstacles including time and distance. Models from meteorology and related sciences have been extensively adapted because the bulk of fungal diseases can become air-borne (SCHRÖDTER, 1960; WAGGONER, 1965; GREGORY, 1972). It may be permitted to refer to these authors for the rather complex models on turbulence, which largely achieve take-off of spores, and spore diffusion. Theories on spore diffusion, gradients of deposition and infection have become mathematically tractable, and have made dispersal predictable if parameters can be measured.

Once spores have become air-borne other conditions prevail. SCHRÖDTER (1960) combining Stoke's law of movement of sphere-shaped particles in calm air and Falck's experience with ellipsoid fungal spores, derived an equation for the fall velocity of ellipsoid spores in calm air as

$$c = \frac{2sg}{9\eta} \sqrt[3]{a} \cdot b \sqrt[3]{b^2} \tag{43}$$

with the term $2sg/9\eta$, being a constant (Stoke's law), c, therefore, depends entirely on length a and width b of spores in μ. This parameter plays an important role in models on the flight line of spores, range of flight, height of flight, and duration of flight (SCHRÖDTER, 1960).

In the flight of air-borne spores one can differentiate between "*probable*" line, range, height, and duration (SCHRÖDTER, 1960). For the probable flight line Schrödter expands Schmidt's equation, on condition that at time $t = 0$ and at place $x = 0$, a number N of spores is dispersed in the open space $z = 0$, the number of spores n' found above z at time t is given by

$$n' = \int_z^\infty n\, dz = \frac{2N}{\sqrt{4\pi at}} \exp\left(-\frac{c^2 t}{4a}\right) \int_z^\infty \exp\left(-\frac{z^2}{4at} - \frac{c}{2a} z\right) dz \tag{44}$$

with $a = A/\delta$. From this Schrödter eventually arrives at

$$z = 0.4769 \sqrt{\frac{4Ax}{\delta U} - \frac{c}{U} \cdot x} \tag{45}$$

as the equation of the probable flight line. Cutting out the shape of the flight line which here proved to be a parabola (see SCHRÖDTER, 1960, p. 181, for details), we reach the determining equation for the probable flight range

$$x = \frac{4AU}{\delta c^2} (0.4769)^2 \tag{46}$$

$$= 0.91 \frac{AU}{\delta c^2}$$

A (coefficient of mass exchange) and δ density are to be read from meteorological tables, U is the wind speed measured by an anemometer and $c =$ the fall velocity of spores can be calculated from spore lengths and widths according to the above equation.

Probable height of flight

$$\frac{dz}{dt} = 0.4769 \sqrt{4a} \cdot \frac{1}{2\sqrt{t}} - c = 0 \quad \text{and}$$

$$t = \frac{(0.4769)^2}{4} \cdot \frac{4a}{c^2}$$

and, finally,

$$z_{max} = 0.2274 = \frac{A}{\delta c} \tag{47}$$

Probable duration of flight

$$0.4769 \sqrt{4a\tau} - c\tau = 0 \tag{48}$$

and, finally,

$$\tau = 0.91 \frac{A}{\delta c^2}. \tag{49}$$

All these models, however, apply to idealized conditions only, but not to eddies, obstacles, and particle stir-up from the ground surface. SCHRÖDTER (1960) departing from FORTAK (1957), who treated this problem in a theory of dust transfer over a dust-active earth surface, also puts forward models for the two latter cases.

How does the spore concentration change when wind blows over a heavily sporulating diseased field? If, for example, $x \geq d$, (SCHRÖDTER, 1960, p. 216/17) (d = width of the spore producing strip, x = width of spore receiving strip in meters etc.), then eventually

$$\sigma = \frac{C}{s} \left[4i^2 \operatorname{erfc} \sqrt{X-D} - 4i^2 \operatorname{erfc} \sqrt{X} \right] \tag{50}$$

with $z = 0$, for previously spore-free fields in which functions as erfc x or ierfc x are known from the theory of heat conduction, σ = number of spores per volume unit, C = the dimension of spore stir-up or spore filtration, s = fall velocity of spores, X = distance, D = spore active strip = $s^2 d / 4\eta U$, with η = exchange coefficient in cm^2/sec., U = wind speed in m/sec. For $x < d$ a somewhat different equation emerges. And the filter effects of wind shelter strips are

$$\sigma = \frac{1}{s} \left[(C_1 + C_2) \, 4i^2 \operatorname{erfc} \sqrt{X} - C_2 \right] \tag{51}$$

within strips,

$$\sigma = \frac{1}{s} \left[(C_1 + C_2) \, 4i^2 \operatorname{erfc} \sqrt{X} - C_2 4i^2 \operatorname{erfc} \sqrt{X-B} \right] \tag{52}$$

at the leeward side of the strips, and B', the width within which total filtration occurs, e. g. a wind defense strip, finally is

$$B' = \left(4i^2 \operatorname{erfc}^{-1} \cdot \frac{C_1}{C^1 + C_2} \right)^2 . \tag{53}$$

Long distance dispersal is much more complicated by irregularities (of turbulence, inversion, rain etc.) in the vertical direction than is focal spread for which the simple statistical methods do not provide (WAGGONER, 1965). However, here also meteorological studies and studies related to diffusionary processes of particles in the air have resulted in a practical equation developed by Pasquill for atomic fall-out etc.(WAGGONER, 1965), which regards the spore cloud as a "plume", and the concentration Co on its axis from a continuous point source of 1 "unit" $\min^{-1}$ is

$$Co = \frac{2.8 \times 10^{-3}}{ud\theta h} \quad \text{units } m^{-3} \tag{54}$$

where u is wind speed (m sec^{-1}), d distance (km), θ the lateral spread (degrees) and h the vertical spread (m) of spores, both the latter measured to the limit where concentration falls to 1/10 the axial concentration.

5. Prediction of Epidemic Events and Control Measures

It is one of the characteristics of models that they generate predictions, which are more or less precise, and/or practical. Of prime interest are predictions regarding the structures of an epidemic, its interactions and regulations and their effects. Most promising for their exploration is systems analysis, though the majority of the presently available models still emanate from linear statistics. Only systems analysis provides models that are dynamic and integrating, and therefore can reveal the interaction in the structures of an epidemic. We feel there can be hardly any argument against systems analysis itself—but quite a lot about the "how", as WAGGONER will explain.

Both parameter estimation and analysis of cause-effect pathways contribute to these ends and finally make the manipulation and the control of epidemics possible. The latter is essentially an "optimization" problem, i.e., finding maxima or minima of functions for "optimal control of system operators" (KOWAL, 1971). Prediction in this context can either refer to the future course of an epidemic as a consequence of a known state of disease (disease forecasting would be a case in point), or one can predict the effect of parameters manipulated by experiments, or disease control, on other structures of the disease and the resulting epidemic. Integrated disease control would greatly benefit from such an optimization. It could provide a guideline for the determination of optimal treatment (kind, time, dose) as well as for the evaluation of their absolute and relative effects. At present optimization in epidemiology is still in its infancy. Progress to this end is being made by attempts to simulate epidemics.

Simulation of epidemics can be achieved (KRANZ, 1973) by

1. Equations derived from multivariate regression,
2. Analog computer,
3. Systems analysis, which WAGGONER will discuss in detail at the end of this book, and
4. Phytotrons and other analogs, which we shall not deal with here.

Simulations based on models derived from multivariate analysis surprisingly prove that only 2–4 variables suffice to reproduce arithmetically the course of an epidemic. It is clearly common in ecology, medical and plant epidemiology that simple models with less than a handful of variables generate results which fit observed facts closely. PIELOU (1969) gives 3 reasons why we so often have such a great similarity between simple mathematical models and the behavior of epidemics: "(1) The factors neglected may indeed be of negligible importance ... (2) Some of the neglected factors cancel one another out. (3) The resemblance of a model to the real-life process it is intended to represent may not be as close as it seems to be."

These questions must be answered after every apparently successful attempt at model building—either by recycling experiments or, perhaps, systems analyses. These simulations are, of course, only black boxes. They can hardly explain much of the intricate cause-effect pathways. Nevertheless, all those interested in prognosis are satisfied with these results, as they serve their purpose. However, such a simulation is not necessarily suitable for a straightforward prognosis, as Waggoner will show.

On the other hand a prediction from a regression line is only permissible as interpolation within the domain of x on the abscissa. Extrapolation by simulators beyond the situation measured either requires (1) thresholds, (2) appropriate probability parameters or (3) specific models of disease progress curves ("shoemakers lasts"). Analog computers are also, in a double sense, "black boxes" and do not reveal much about the many interactions of pathogen, host environment and control factors, in the course of an epidemic. But they can predict changes in disease development if parameters of a few variables are altered by turning buttons. ANALYTIS (1973) has used an analog computer to analyze the effect of some growth functions on the transformation of disease progress curves (p. 22). Analog computers require differential or algebraic equations as models to become operationable as quick tools for analytical and simulation purposes.

Three specific objectives of mathematical analysis and modeling deserve a closer look in this context: Forecasting (5.1.), predicting the efficiency of control measures (5.2), and appraisal of crop losses (5.3.). A number of models relating to the prediction of the danger of infection from neighboring fields have been quoted already in the text (4.4.2).

5.1 Forecasting

Forecasting of disease outbreak or development, infection and latent periods, and such like, has been one of the major preoccupation of plant pathologists during the past fifty years. However, not all forecasting rules necessarily require mathematics. Some are entirely empirical and derived from straight-forward weather observation, as for instance most of the early forecasting rules for potato late blight. Other rules are based on the disease development or cycle itself as with the yellow streaks of the Sigatoka disease of bananas for the determination of the next date of spraying mineral oil (KLEIN, 1960; KRANZ, 1968). We cannot review all possible approaches of disease forecasting here, as we are only interested in mathematical models, but one may consult WAGGONER (1960) and BOURKE (1970).

Mathematical forecasting models are still largely based on linear regressions, mostly partial or multivariate analyses. Lag correlations have also been used (MOGK, 1973; STEINER, 1973), and as a check of variables extracted by a multivariate analysis a principle component analysis (SEAL, 1966) has been employed (ANALYTIS, 1973). Some examples of forecasting models will be presented in Tables 4–8.

Most models are of local importance. One of the forecasting models that has — geographically — a wider application is a so-called "negative prognosis" for late blight in West Germany [SCHRÖDTER and ULLRICH (1965); ULLRICH and SCHRÖDTER (1966)]. This has been run since 1967 by the Deutscher Wetterdienst, Offenbach, for whole of the Federal Republic, and is probably the first large scale computer-aided practical scheme in plant pathology. The model is

$$\sum_{t=1}^{t=n} f(p)_t = 150 \text{ (or 270)} \tag{55}$$

where $f(p)$ is the disease score per week, $t = 1, 2, \ldots n$ the weeks after emergence of potatoes till the week t_n before disease outbreak. This is defined as 0.1% (or 1%) attack, which is equivalent to a logit $150 \cdot 10^{-2}$. The model represents the sum of the weekly functions of weighted parameters

$$Y = c_1 y(K_D) + c_2 y(S_D) + c_3 y(M) + c_4 y(U) \tag{56}$$

for which the parameters have been derived from about 6 years of country-wide and specially designed experiments (see also pp. 95 and 96).

Forecasting models may well be intermediate products of a study of causal relationship (Fig. 4). They are, however, acceptable as long as they serve their purpose and are not mistaken as describing the real causes. Sometimes these models actually comprise variables which are not at all biologically relevant — BUTT and ROYLE (p. 109) and WAGGONER (p. 138) are going to treat this phenomenon. Yet the forecaster might be happy with them, having an attitude somewhat different from the researcher interested in causal pathways of epidemics.

5.1.1 Inoculum. The prediction of available inoculum (e.g. the amount of infectious propagules), either of initial inoculum (at the beginning of the susceptible period of the host) or any later inoculum can be of utmost importance for disease control. However, very few mathematical models are known; some are given in Table 4. Normally one tries to rely on measurements (p. 14). In the future fully-fledged simulators with verified parameters should be able to generate predictions of inoculum available at a given time.

5.1.2 Infection, Incubation and Latent Period. These are equally important elements of an epidemic and to be able to predict as accurately as possible is highly desirable also for practical purposes. But here also useful models are rare so far. A solution of these problems may also be expected from systems analysis which comprises the appropriate details in its output. Table 5 summarizes some published models.

5.1.3 The Progress of the Epidemic. The future course of an epidemic known to the plant pathologist would greatly help to gear control measures. It also would permit an estimate of the damage to be expected if treatment is discontinued, and similar consequences. We leave this aspect to be elaborated on further by the three last chapters of this book. For some models see Table 6.

5.2 The Efficiency of Control Measures

Control measures in plant pathology comprise cultural methods, host resistance, fungicides, including seed dressing, some few physical methods, like soil fumigation, cutting and burning of diseased plants or parts thereof, but hardly any biological control so far. They are either aimed against the initial, overwintering inoculum, y_0, and or against the multiplication rate r of the pathogen (VAN DER PLANK, 1963). Sanitation is a typical example of the former, horizontal resistance and protective fungicides of the latter. For some of the equations to estimate effects of resistance, fungicides and adverse weather conditions see Table 7.

5.2.1 Sanitation. We have already discussed this aspect under 4.3.1. Van der Plank's model is versatile enough to serve both ends, analysis of structures and prediction of effects, if used relevantly.

5.2.2 Horizontal Resistance. Whereas vertical or race-specific resistance, also affects y_0 as does sanitation (p. 26), horizontal resistance, or race nonspecific-resistance, affects the multiplication rate r. Protective fungicides and spells of adverse weather work the same way. VAN DER PLANK (1963, 1967, 1968) who coined these terms, also proposed a number of models explaining and analyzing their action by means of his r_l and r (p. 30). The strength of genes confering vertical resistance can be measured by the relative half life of races (VAN DER PLANK, 1968). For this estimation two races are compared in mixtures under identical conditions after each generation (cycle) in relative numbers, and the linear regression coefficient b is calculated. The half time is $\lg 0.5 = -0.301$ and the half time of race B relative to race A is $-0.301/b$ generations (or cycles). Whether horizontal and/or vertical resistance is present in a variety can be tested by an analysis of variance (VAN DER PLANK, 1968) or by the course of an epidemic (ROBINSON, 1968).

These models only mark a beginning. Much sharper tools are needed and can be expected, to elucidate efficiency, and implications of resistance on the dynamics of pathogen and lesion populations. Nothing, except one attempt by KIYOSAWA and SHIYOMI (1972) (Table 7), is known of mathematical approximation to epidemic cycles of introduced diseases in a number of subsequent years. Here, as perhaps in other cases, Fourrier analyses or oscillations might be appropriate. Approximations of rhythmic curves should also be envisaged for models expressing crop vulnerability, and the longevity of a new resistant variety.

Table 6. Some proposed equations to estimate disease progress[a]

Disease	Host	Equation	Terms	Authors
Blister blight	tea	$y = 33 + 0.3145 x_1 - 0.03725 x_1 x_2$	y = number of blisters per 100 shoots about 3 weeks ahead, x_1 = spores caught per unit volume of air, x_2 = mean daily sunshine	Kerr and Rodrigo (1967)
Stripe rust	wheat	$\lg n_t = -\lg [x_1 + pmx_1^p - (p+i) mx_1^{p+i}] + t \lg \dfrac{1}{x_1}$	n_t = number of lesions at time t, p = latent period in days, m = number of new infections per day, i = infectious periods in days, x_1 = positive simple root	Oort (1968)
Stem rust	wheat	$x_n = x_0 \displaystyle\sum_{i=0}^{n} R^i$ or $\dfrac{x_n}{x_0} = \dfrac{1 - R^{n+1}}{1 - R}$	x_n = number of sporulating and old, non-sporulating pustules, x_0 = initial number of sporulating and old, non-sporulating pustules, n = number of rust generations, R = number of new pustules produced per actively sporulating pustule in the previous generation. This is considered an improvement on van der Plank's compound interest model making allowance for the delay.	Leonard (1969)
Leaf rust	wheat	$y = -3.3998 + 0.0606 x_1 + 0.7675 x_2 + 0.4003 x_3 + 0.0077 x_4$	y = lg % leaf rust severity 14 days after date of prediction (DP), x_1 = average hours of dew or rain on leaves per day during the 7 days before DP, x_2 = lg % leaf rust severity on DP, x_3 = growth stage of wheat in integers from 1–9, x_4 = Schrödter's temperature equivalence (p. 9).	Burleigh et al. (1972)

Disease	Crop	Equation	Description	Reference
Blast	rice	$\lambda = \dfrac{T}{2} r + ln\,\theta$	The authors propose 9 more prediction models for winter or spring wheat, various predictive periods (in days ahead) and rust or no rust at DP, all with changing sets of variables. λ = yearly infection rate, $\theta = y_0/Y_T$ (initial number divided by final number of lesions), r = infection rate, T = number of days of host's vegetation period where infection is possible	KIYOSAWA (1972)
Apple scab	apple	$y = 0.08017 + 0.009\,W_{i-b}(\text{sk}) + 0.00211\,H_{2(i-10)}$	y = Rate of change in disease severity; $W_{i-b}(\text{sk}) = \sum_{i=1}^{n} f(x_i)$ = spore germination function at date i minus the incubation period b in days, n number of hours with leaf wetness and $f(x_i)$ the temperature equivalent by Schröder, $H_{2(i-10)}$ = frequency of hours with temp. 18–20 °C 10 days before disease reading.	ANALYTIS (1973)
Coffee berry disease	coffee	$y_{max} = 1.1645 + 2.1582 x_1 - 0.3276 x_2$	y_{max} = maximum disease frequency, x_1 = disease frequency in % in the endosperm stage of growing fruits, x_2 = disease frequency in % in the hard green stage of growing fruits.	MOGK (1973)
Coffee berry disease	coffee	$y = -0.0271 + 0.0886x$	y = transformed ($y' = \lg 1/1 - \sqrt{y_i}$) disease frequency in %, x = relative susceptibility $=(0.2/T_i)\,Y_{max}$ with T as dry matter of fruits at time i and Y_{max} as maximum disease at time i.	MOGK (1973)

[a] Other than VAN DER PLANK's (1963) models and those already mentioned in the text, see also JOWETT et al.

Table 7. Some equations proposed to estimate and predict effects of resistance[a], fungicides, and environmental factors

Disease	Host	Equation	Terms	Authors
Late blight	potatoes	$Y_D = \left[\sum_{k=1}^{m} b_k F(D_k) \right]_{(n-i)b}$	Y_D = Effect of leaf wetness or high humidity on infection (change of disease incidence), b_k = frequency of leaf wetness duration of at least k hours, i = incubation period in days, $F(D_k)$ = regression of leaf wetness duration on disease increase in a cubic polynom, n = date, b = 7 days	SCHRÖDTER and ULLRICH (1965)
Late blight	potatoes	$Y_U = [a_0 - a_1 h_m]_{(n-i)b}$	Y_U = Effect of dry periods on survival of sporangia h_m = frequency of hours with humidity below 70%, a_0 and a_1 number of sporangia at the beginning and end of dry period.	SCHRÖDTER and ULLRICH (1965)
Stem rust	oat	$r_m = r_s + \dfrac{n}{t} \ln m$	r_m = rate of rust increase in a plot of multiline varieties (host mixture), r_s = rate of rust increase in a plot of susceptible variety, m = the proportion of susceptible plants in a host mixture, n = number of rust generations, t = number of days of rust increase	LEONARD (1969)
Stem rust	oat	$\lg \dfrac{q_n}{1-q_n} = \lg \dfrac{q_0}{1-q_0} - n \lg(1-s)$	changes in proportion of two races q, (e.g. race 2), and $1-q$ (e.g. race 1), where n = number of generations, q_0 and $1-q_0$, respectively = initial proportion of both races, s = a constant. Plotting $q_n/(1-q_n)$ against n gives a straight line with $a = \lg q_0/(1-q_0)$ and $b = -\lg(1-s)$	LEONARD (1969a)

Disease	Crop	Equation	Description	Reference
Blast	rice		Two equations (see Table 6) used to predict longevity in years of a variety with true plus field resistance (where true resistance affects y_0 and field resistance r)	KIYOSAWA (1972, 1972a)
Blast	rice	$y = \beta e^{-\alpha d}$	y = dispersal gradient, β = number of lesions on the initial source plant after the 1. generation, α = a constant determining the dispersal gradient, d = distance from the initial source plant	KIYOSAWA and SHIYOMI (1972)
Blast	rice	$$y_i^{(t)} = \gamma[y_0^{(i-1)} e^{-ja} + \sum_{k=1}^{\infty} y_k^{(i-1)}(e^{-|k-j|a} + e^{-|k-j|a})]$$ $$\gamma = \frac{4(1 + 2\sum_{d=1}^{\infty} e^{-0.1d})}{1 + 2\sum_{d=1}^{\infty} e^{-ad}}$$ (with terms as in the above equation), $\gamma y_0^{(i-1)} e^{-ja}$ = amount of effective spores the j-th plant receives from source, $\gamma y_k^{(i-1)} e^{-|k+j|a}$ from the k-th plant on the same side from the source and the last term refers to the inoculum received from the k-th plant on the opposite side of the point. $$y^{(t)} = 2\sum_{j=0}^{\infty} y_j^{(i)} - y_0^{(i)}$$ $y^{(t)}$ = total number of "susceptible type" lesions after the i-th generation.	$y_i^{(t)}$ = number of "susceptible type" lesions after the i-th generation on the γ-th plant from the source, KIYOSAWA and SHIYOMI (1972)

Table 7 (continued)

Disease	Host	Equation	Terms	Authors
Blast	rice	$T/T' = v\lambda_c'/\lambda_c$	T/T' = relation between longevity of mixed cultivation and rotation with the same varieties, λ_c and λ_c' the rates of increase of lesions, respectively, T = longevity of rotation and cultivation of lines $v = \dfrac{v}{\lambda_c}(ln\,M - ln\,k_c)$, where k_c = amount of pathogen on the c lines in the first year of cultivation of the lines included in the comparison in pure stands, and $M = k_i e^{\lambda_i T_i}$ where T_i is the time at which the number of lesions reaches M and the line in pure cultivation becomes useless $T' = \dfrac{1}{\lambda_c'}(ln\,M' - ln\,k_c')$ for mixed cultivation	KIYOSAWA (1972b)
Coffee berry disease	coffee	$y = 26.068 - 0.0357x_1 + 0.174x_2$	y = number of new infections, x_1 = efficiency of Orthodifolatan as a function of time [0,1], 1 = efficiency in germination tests immediately after spraying, x_2 = hours of leaf wetness at temperatures $\leq 10°$ C	STEINER (1973)

[a] Other than VAN DER PLANK's (1967, 1968) models.

5.3 Appraisal of Crop Losses

Epidemiology will be increasingly challenged in the future by the need to establish proper and accurate disease severity/yield loss relationships. They are needed, *inter alia,* for decision-making in crop protection. The contribution of epidemiology in this context lies in the explanation of the behavior of populations of lesions in relation to crop physiology, and in the methodology of measuring disease. Plant physiologists and rural economists must also show interest. Some models have been proposed already which predict the loss equivalent to disease in certain stages of the host development (Table 8 and BUTT and ROYLE, p. 107).

6. Classification

Classification problems may one day attain great prominence in comparative epidemiology (KRANZ, 1974). As epidemiology deals with populations, it can be useful to delimit more objectively groupings of individuals, strains, races, varieties, treatments, reactions etc., which are more similar in epidemiological behavior amongst themselves than compared with other groupings. To go beyond sheer description and more or less subjective inferences, methods are required which range from set theory (KRANZ and KNAPP, 1973), similarity coefficients, cluster and factor analyses (KRANZ, 1968b; KRANZ and LÖRINCZ, 1970), to perhaps more sophisticated mathematics. All these methods analyze the (measured) components of populations and group them according to their mathematically defined similarity. Their interpretation may require some caution.

The latter authors have made use of the computer program MCEF, CLUS and PAFA, respectively. A multivariate correlation analysis, Principal Factor Analysis (PAFA) with subsequent orthogonal rotation according to the Varimax criteria, was used to test the intercorrelation of structures of disease progress curves. Some empirically known facts could be verified in this way (KRANZ, 1968b).

Another approach to classification is by discriminant analyses. A multiple discriminant analysis and a stepwise discriminant analysis was employed by HINDORF (1973) to separate the components of the *Colletotrichum* population on coffee, under the influence of various factors (see also MOGK, p. 72). KRANZ and KNAPP (1973) have employed sets (Fig. 7) to their study of the influence of higher plant vegetations on the composition of the parasitic mycoflora.

7. Some Remarks on Stochastic Models in Epidemiology

Thus far, satisfactory progress has been made in epidemiology as regards temporal relationships because they can more easily be dealt with and because of their importance. Changes of pathogens and disease in space obviously have been less intriguing until now, apart from spore dispersal (4.4.). Spatial aspects and, even more, space and time aspects, seem to ask for very complex mathematical theories which may prove difficult to work with analytically. Most likely they require stochastic approaches, as "population growth is a stochastic process" (PIELOU, 1969). Yet most models in epidemiology are still deterministic.

Table 8. Some of the equations proposed for the estimation of crop losses due to plant diseases

Diseases	Host	Equations	Terms	Authors
Powdery mildew	spring barley, oat	$y \approx 2.5\,M^{1/2}$ or $2.5\sqrt{y\%}$	y = yield loss in %, M or $y\%$ = % mildew assessed in growth stage 10.5 (Fekes scale)	Large and Doling (1962)
	winter wheat	$y \approx 2.0\,M^{1/2}$		Large and Doling (1963)
Leaf blotch	barley	$L = (0.66x_1 + 0.5x_2)/2$	L = loss in %, x_1 = disease rating for flag leaf, x_2 = disease rating for 2nd leaf from the top.	James et al. (1968)
Stem rust	wheat	$y = -25.53 + 27.17\,\ln x$	y = average % yield loss, x = average % disease severity	Romig and Calpouzos (1970)
Leaf rust	wheat	$\hat{y} = 5.3788 + 5.5260x_2 - 0.3308x_5 + 0.5019x_7$	$\hat{y}$ = loss in % yield, x_2 = % rust per tiller at boot, x_5 = % rust on flag leaf at early berry, x_7 = % rust on flag leaf at early dough	Burleigh et al. (1972)
Late blight	potatoes	$y = 1.867x_1 + 0.446x_2 + 1.144x_3 + 0.628x_4 + 0.193x_5 + 0.343x_8 + 0.829x_9$	y = loss in % (for early infection), $x_1 \ldots x_9$ disease severity on sampling dates $1\ldots 9$	James et al. (1972)
Coffee berry disease	coffee	$y = 84.632 - 0.87x$	y = loss in % berries harvested, x = disease frequency in % in the endosperm stage of the growing fruit	Mogk (1973)

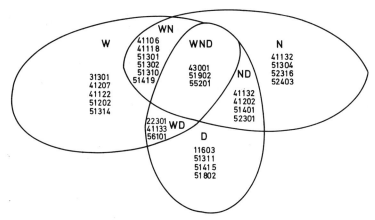

Fig. 7. A Venn diagram showing the distribution of pathogens (code numbers) on various types of vegetation of three localities D, N, W (from KRANZ and KNAPP, 1973)

Stochastic methods—beyond that in statistical methods—have so far enjoyed little attention in epidemiology of plant diseases. VAN DER PLANK (1963) even denies a need, while favoring the deterministic approach. This is justified as long as we really have ample data in hand, or believe we know exactly enough the sizes of the populations involved, and the rates of their change. It may also be justified as long as we are satisfied with the present accuracy of predictions. However, the values for variables and constants derived from measurements are, in fact, limited by their accuracy, and are on each occasion restricted in number. For these reasons each value necessarily carries an element of a probability distribution. Therefore, instead of entering specific though more or less inaccurate parameters, probability functions may be more adequate in generating predictions from our future models. Such models may even be more exact than deterministic ones, because probability statements make allowance for the experimental error, and they permit inferences in probalistic terms (KOWAL, 1971).

It is not too daring to anticipate also in plant epidemiology a great potential of stochastic models, particularly for phenomena varying at random such as infection process or spatial effects. The mathematical handling of stochastic processes has given a new impetus to the study of the "continuous-infection" model in medical epidemiology (BAILEY, 1957). Why not so in plant epidemiology?

Only very few, still rather fumbling attempts, of probalistic methods can be found in the literature. They all refer to spatial problems, such as SCHRÖDTER'S "probable flight range, duration, height, line", which gives every event a 1:1 chance (p. 36). VAN DER PLANK'S (1960) "horizon of infection" expresses the probability that a lesion will form a daughter lesion in unit time on a healthy plant at a distance s is $p = a/s^b$. WAGGONER (1962) proposes stochastic models which allow calculation of the probability involved in the landing of spores in a field and Garrett a similar one for the chance of propagules of soil-borne fungi infecting a root (p. 35).

Advocating more sophisticated models is not just a liking for mathematical "embroideries" as VAN DER PLANK (1967, p. 77) likes to call it. The deeper we intrude into a system called epidemic the more highly structured our models will be, particularly in system analyses. Irrespective of that, one must develop and study simple and often abstract models first before "modifying and complicating" (PIE-LOU, 1969) this basis for elaboration. Very simple and highly tractable mathematical models already often suffice to tackle epidemiological problems, as VAN DER PLANK (1960, 1963, 1967, 1968) has demonstrated. Some even permit systems analysis as shown by ZADOKS (1971) with Van der Plank's corrected basic infection rate, R_c. It might also be acceptable for mathematical models to disregard a statistical rule as long as predictions are somehow realistic. All this is true and perhaps encouraging for some of you to make your own attempts in mathematical models and analyses.

References

ANALYTIS, S.: Methodik der Analyse von Epidemien dargestellt am Apfelschorf [*Venturia inaequalis* (Cooke) Aderh.]. Acta Phytomedica 1, 76 pp. (1973).

ANALYTIS, S.: Zur Einteilung von Schätzklassen für die Befallsstärke von Pflanzenkrankheiten. Phytopath. Z. 76, 319–327 (1973 a).

ANALYTIS, S., KRANZ, J.: Über Korrelationen zwischen Befallshäufigkeit und Befallsstärke bei Pflanzenkrankheiten. Phytopath. Z. 73, 201–207 (1972).

ANALYTIS, S., KRANZ, J.: Bestimmung des optimalen Stichprobenumfanges bei phytopathologischen Untersuchungen. Phytopath. Z. 74, 349–357 (1972 a).

ANALYTIS, S., KRANZ, J., STUMPF, A.: Eine Methode zur Berechnung der Blattfläche. Angew. Botanik 45, 111–114 (1971).

AUST, H. J.: Über die Variabilität von Keimung, Infektion, Inkubations- und Latenzzeit beim echten Mehltau der Gerste (*Erysiphe graminis* DC.f.sp. *hordei* Marchal). Ph.D. Thesis, Univ. Gießen (1973).

AUST, H. J., KRANZ, J.: Einfluß der Konidiendichte auf Keimung, Infektion, Inkubationszeit und Sporulation bei dem echten Mehltau der Gerste (*Erysiphe graminis* DC. f. sp. *hordei* Marchal). Phytopath. Z. (in press).

BAILEY, N. T. J.: The mathematical theory of epidemics. London: Charles Griffin 1957.

BAKER, R.: The dynamics of inoculum. In: Ecology of soil-borne plant pathogens (ed. K. F. BAKER, W. C. SNYDER) pp. 395–403. London: John Murrey 1965.

BAKER, R.: Analyses involving inoculum density of soil-borne plant pathogens in epidemiology. Phytopathology 61, 1280–1292 (1971).

BAKER, R., MAURER, C. L., MAURER, R. A.: Ecology of plant pathogens in soil. VII. Mathematical models and inoculum density. Phytopathology 57, 662–666 (1967).

BALD, J. G.: Measurement of host reactions to soil-borne inoculum. In: Root diseases and soilborne pathogens. (ed. T. A. TOUSSOUN, R. V. BEGA, P. E. NELSON) pp. 37–41. Berkeley, Los Angeles, London: Univ. of California Press 1970.

BLEIHOLDER, H.: Beiträge zur Epidemiologie von *Cercospora beticola* Sacc. an Zuckerrüben. Ph. D. Thesis Univ. Bonn (1971).

BOURKE, P. M., AUSTIN: Use of weather information in the prediction of plant disease epiphytotics. Ann. Rev. Phytophat. 8, 345–370 (1970).

BURLEIGH, J. R., EVERSMEYER, M. G., ROELFS, H. P.: Development of linear equations for predicting wheat leaf rust. Phytopathology 62, 947–953 (1972).

CASWELL, H. C., KOENIG, H. E., RESH, J. A., ROSS, Q. E.: An introduction to systems science for ecologists. In: Systems analysis and simulation in ecology (ed. B. C. PATTEN) vol. II, pp. 3–78. New York, London: Academic Press 1972.

COCHRAN, W. C.: Sampling techniques. 2nd ed. New York, London, Sydney: Wiley & Sons 1963.

COHEN, M., YARWOOD, C. E.: Temperature response of fungi as a straight line transformation. Plant Physiol. 27, 634–638 (1952).

DIMOND, A. E., HORSFALL, J. G.: Inoculum and the diseased population. In: Plant Pathology. An advanced treatise (ed. J. G. HORSFALL, A. E. DIMOND) vol. III, pp. 1–22. New York, London: Academic Press 1960.

DIMOND, A. E., HORSFALL, J. G.: The theory of inoculum. In: Ecology of soil-borne plant pathogens (ed. K. F. BAKER, W. C. SNYDER) pp. 404–415. London: John Murrey 1965.

DIRKS, V. A., ROMIG, R. W.: Linear models applied to variation in numbers of cereal rust spores. Phytopathology 60, 246–251 (1970).

EVANS, G. Clifford: The quantitative analysis of plant growth. Oxford, London, Edinburgh, Melbourne: Blackwell 1972.

EVERSMEYER, M. G., BURLEIGH, J. R.: A method of predicting epidemic development of wheat leaf rust. Phytopathology 60, 805–811 (1970).

FORTAK, H.: Staubtransporte über staubaktiver Erdoberfläche. Z. Meteorol. 11, 19–27 (1957).

GÄUMANN, E.: Pflanzliche Infektionslehre. 2nd ed. Basel: Birkhäuser 1951.

GEIGER, R.: Das Klima der bodennahen Luftschichten. 4th ed. Braunschweig: Vieweg 1961.

GIBBS, J. N.: Inoculum sources for coffee berry disease. Ann. appl. Biol. 64, 515–522 (1969).

GREGORY, P. H.: Interpreting plant disease dispersal gradients. Ann. Rev. Phytopath. 6, 189–212 (1968).

GREGORY, P. H.: Microbiology of the atmosphere. 2nd ed. London: Leonhard Hill 1972.

GREIG-SMITH, P.: Quantitative plant ecology. 2nd ed. London: Butterworth 1964.

HABGOOD, R. M.: Designation of physiological races of plant pathogens. Nature 227, 2168–1269 (1970).

HANSEN, M. H., HURWITZ, W. H., MADOW, W. G.: Sample survey methods and theory. vol. I. Methods and application. New York, London, Sidney: Wiley & Sons 1953.

HINDORF, H.: Colletotrichum population auf Coffea arabica L. in Kenia. I. Eine Methode zur systematischen Trennung von Pilzpopulationen. Phytopath. Z. 77, 97–116 (1973).

HIRST, J. M., STEDMAN, O. J., HOGG, W. H.: Long distance spore transport: methods of measurement, vertical spore profiles and the detection of immigrant spores. J. gen. Microbiol. 48, 329–355 (1967).

HORSFALL, J. G., BARRATT, R. W.: An improved grading system for measuring plant diseases. Phytopathology 35, 655 (1945).

INGOLD, C. T.: Dispersal by air and water—the take-off. In: Plant Pathology. An advanced treatise (ed. J. G. HORSFALL, DIMOND, A. E.) vol. III. pp. 137–168. New York, London: Academic Press 1960.

JAMES, W. C., JENKINS, J. E. E., JEMMETT, J. L.: The relationship between leaf blotch caused by Rhynchosporium secalis and losses in grain yield of spring barley. Ann. appl. Biol. 62, 273–288 (1968).

JAMES, W. C., SHIH, C. S., HODGSON, W. A., CALLBECK, L. C.: The quantitative relationship between late blight of potato and loss in tuber yield. Phytopathology 62, 92–96 (1972).

KAY, R. H.: Experimental biology. Measurement and analysis. London: Chapman & Hall 1966.

KERR, A., RODRIGO, W. R. F.: Epidemiology of tea blister blight (Exobasidium vexans). III. Spore deposition and disease prediction. Trans. Br. mycol. Soc. 50, 49–55 (1967).

KERR, A., SHANMUGANATHAN, N.: Epidemiology of tea blister blight (Exobasidium vexans). I. Sporulation. Trans. Br. mycol. Soc. 49, 139–145 (1966).

KIYOSAWA, S.: Effect of addition of field resistance to variety with true resistance. Japan. J. Breed. 22, 140–146 (1972).

KIYOSAWA, S.: Theoretical comparison between mixture and rotation cultivations of disease-resistant varieties. Ann. Phytopath. Soc. Japan 38, 52–59 (1972).

KIYOSAWA, S.: Mathematical studies on the curve of disease increase. Ann. Phytopath. Soc. Japan 38, 30–40 (1972a).

KIYOSAWA, S., SHIYOMI, M.: A theoretical evaluation of mixing resistant variety with susceptible variety for controlling plant diseases. Ann. Phytopath. Soc. Japan 38, 41–51 (1972).

KLEIN, H. H.: Control of *Cercospora* leaf spot of banana with application of oil sprays based on the disease cycle. Phytopathology 50, 488–490 (1960).

KOWAL, N. E.: A rationale for modeling dynamic ecological systems. In: Systems analysis and simulation in ecology (ed. B. C. PATTEN) vol. I, pp. 123–194. New York, London: Academic Press 1971.

KRANZ, J.: Zur Konidienbildung und -verbreitung bei *Mycosphaerella musicola* Leach. Z. Pflanzenkrankh. 75, 327–338 (1968).

KRANZ, J.: Eine Analyse von annuellen Epidemien pilzlicher Parasiten. I. Die Befallskurven und ihre Abhängigkeit von einigen Umweltfaktoren. Phytopath. Z. 61, 59–86 (1968a).

KRANZ, J.: Eine Analyse von annuellen Epidemien pilzlicher Parasiten. III. Über Korrelationen zwischen quantitativen Merkmalen von Befallskurven und Ähnlichkeiten von Epidemien. Phytopath. Z. 61, 205–217 (1968b).

KRANZ, J.: Schätzklassen für Krankheitsbefall. Phytopath. Z. 61, 131–139 (1970).

KRANZ, J.: Zur Einteilung von Schätzklassen für Befallswerte. Paper read at VII. Int. Plant Protection Congr. Paris (1970a).

KRANZ, J.: Einige Voraussetzungen für die Planung und Durchführung von Feldversuchen in der Epidemiologie. Z. Pflanzenkrankh. 79, 573–581 (1972).

KRANZ, J.: Epidemiology, concepts and scope. Current trends in plant pathology (ed. S. P. RAYCHAUDHURI, J. P. VERMA) pp. 26–32. Lucknow: Dept. Botany, Univ. of Lucknow 1973.

KRANZ, J.: Comparison of epidemics. Annu. Rev. Phytopath. 12 (1974).

KRANZ, J., KNAPP, R.: Qualitative und quantitative Unterschiede in der Vergesellschaftung parasitischer Pilzarten in verschiedenen Vegetationseinheiten. Phytopath. Z. 77, 235–251 (1973).

KRANZ, J., LÖRINCZ, D.: Methoden zum automatischen Vergleich epidemischer Abläufe bei Pflanzenkrankheiten. Phytopath. Z. 67, 225–233 (1970).

KRANZ, J., MOGK, M., STUMPF, A.: EPIVEN—ein Simulator für Apfelschorf. Z. Pflanzenkrankh. 80, 181–187 (1973).

LARGE, E. C.: Measuring plant disease. Ann. Rev. Phytopath. 4, 9–28 (1966).

LARGE, E. C., DOLING, D. A.: The measurement of cereal mildew and its effect on yield. Plant Pathol. 11, 47–57 (1962).

LARGE, E. C., DOLING, D. A.: Effect of mildew on yield of winter wheat. Plant Pathol. 12, 128–130 (1963).

LAVILLE, E., LOSSOIS, P.: Méthode de Van der Plank et mode de propagation du Bayoud. Fruits 18, 249–253 (1963).

LEONARD, K. J.: Factors affecting rates of stem rust increase in mixed plantings of susceptible and resistant oat varieties. Phytopathology 59, 1845–1850 (1969).

LEONARD, K. J.: Selection in heterogeneous populations of *Puccinia graminis* f. sp. *aveae*. Phytopathology 59, 1851–1857 (1969a).

MALOY, O. C., ALEXANDER, M.: The "most probable number" method for estimating populations of plant pathogen organism in soil. Phytopathology 48, 126–128 (1958).

MAY, K. R.: Physical aspects of sampling air-borne microbes. In: Air-borne microbes (ed. P. H. GREGORY, J. L. MONTEITH) pp. 60–80 (1967).

MOGK, M.: Untersuchungen zur Epidemiologie von *Colletotrichum coffeanum* Noack sensu Hindorf in Kenia, eine Analyse der Wirt-Parasit-Umwelt-Beziehungen. Ph.D. Thesis, Univ. Gießen (1973).

MÜLLER, K. O.: Theoretische Betrachtungen zur Epidemiologie anemochorischer Pflanzenkrankheiten. Z. Pflanzenkrankh. 64, 402–407 (1957).

MUENCH, H.: Catalytic models in epidemiology. Cambridge, Mass.: Harvard Univ. Press 1959.

OORT, H. J. P.: A model of the early stage of epidemics. Neth. J. Pl. Path. 74, 177–180 (1968).

PLATT, R. B., GRIFFITHS, J. F.: Environmental measurement and interpretation. New York, Cincinnati, Toronto, London, Melbourne: Van Nostrand Reinhold Co. 1969.

PIELOU, E. C.: An introduction to mathematical ecology. New York, London, Sydney, Toronto: Wiley-Interscience 1969.

ROBINSON, R. A.: The concept of vertical and horizontal resistance as illustrated by bacterial wilt of potatoes. Commonwealth Mycological Institute Kew; Phytopathological Papers No 10 (1968).

ROMIG, R. W., CALPOUZOS, L.: The relationship between stem rust and loss in yield of spring wheat. Phytopathology 60, 1801–1805 (1970).

ROYLE, D. J.: Quantitative relationships between infection by the hop downy mildew pathogen *Pseudoperonospora humuli,* and weather and inoculum factors. Ann. appl. Biol. 73, 19–30 (1973).

ROYLE, D. J., THOMAS, G. E.: Analysis of relationships between weather factors and concentrations of air-borne sporangia of *Pseudoperonospora humuli,* Trans. Br. mycol. Soc. 58, 79–89 (1972).

SCHRÖDTER, H.: Dispersal by air and water—the flight and landing. In: Plant Pathology. An advanced treatise (ed. J. G. HORSFALL, A. E. DIMOND) vol. III, pp. 169–227. New York, London: Academic Press 1960.

SCHRÖDTER, H.: Methodisches zur Bearbeitung phytometeoropathologischer Untersuchungen, dargestellt am Beispiel der Temperaturrelation. Phytopath. Z. 53, 154–166 (1965).

SCHRÖDTER, H., ULLRICH, J.: Untersuchungen zur Biometeorologie und Epidemiologie von *Phytophthora infestans* (Mont.) de By. auf mathematisch-statistischer Grundlage. Phytopath. Z. 54, 87–103 (1965).

SCHRÖDTER, H., ULLRICH, J.: Das Problem der Vorhersage des Auftretens der Kartoffelkrautfäule *(Phytophthora infestans)* und die Möglichkeit seiner Lösung durch die „Negativ-Prognose". Nachrichtenbl. Deutsch. Pflanzenschutzd. 18, 33–40 (1966).

SEAL, H. L.: Multivariate statistical analysis for biologists. London: Methuen 1966.

SNEH, B., KATAN, J., HENIS, Y., WAHL, I.: Methods for evaluating inoculum density of *Rhizoctonia* in naturally infested soil. Phytopathology 56, 74–78 (1966).

STEINER, K. G.: Wechselwirkung zwischen Witterung, Wirt, Parasit und Fungiziden bei der Kaffeekirschen-Krankheit (*Colletotrichum coffeanum* Noack). Ph. D. Thesis, Gießen (1973).

STEUBING, L.: Pflanzenökologisches Praktikum. Berlin und Hamburg: Parey 1965.

VAN DER PLANK, J. E.: A method for estimating the number of random groups of adjacent diseased plants in a homogeneous field. Trans. Roy. Soc. South. Africa 31, 369–278 (1947).

VAN DER PLANK, J. E.: Analysis of epidemics. In: Plant Pathology. An advanced treatise (ed. J. G. HORSFALL, A. E. DIMOND) vol. III, pp. 229–289. New York, London: Academic Press 1960.

VAN DER PLANK, J. E.: Plant diseases: Epidemics and control. New York, London: Academic Press 1963.

VAN DER PLANK, J. E.: Epidemiology of fungicidal action. In: Fungicides. An advanced treatise (ed. D. C. TORGESON) vol. I, pp. 63–92. New York, London: Academic Press 1967.

VAN DER PLANK, J. E.: Disease resistance in plants. New York, London: Academic Press 1968.

VERMEULEN, H.: Coffee berry disease in Kenya. I. *Colletotrichum* spp. colonizing the bark of *Coffea arabica.* Neth. J. Plant. Path. 76, 277–284 (1970).

WADSWORTH, R. M. (ed.): The measurement of environmental factors in terrestrial ecology. Oxford, Edinburgh: Blackwell 1968.

WAGGONER, P. E.: Distribution of potato late blight around inoculum sources. Phytopathology 42, 323–328 (1952).

WAGGONER, P. E.: Forecasting epidemics. In: Plant Pathology. An advanced treatise (ed. J. G. HORSFALL, A. E. DIMOND) vol. III, pp. 291–312. New York, London: Academic Press 1960.

WAGGONER, P. E.: Weather, space, time and chance of infection. Phytopathology 52, 1100–1108 (1962).

WAGGONER, P. E.: Microclimate and plant disease. Ann. Rev. Phytopath. 3, 103–126 (1965).

WESTCOTT, J. H.: Estimation of values of parameters of a model to conform with observations. In: Models and analogs in biology (ed. J. W. L. BEAMENT) pp. 102–121. Cambridge: University Press 1960.

YATES, F.: Sampling methods for censuses and surveys. 3rd ed. London: Griffin 1971.

ZADOKS, J. C.: Yellow rust on wheat, studies in epidemiology and physiologic specialization Tijdschr. Pl. Ziekten (Neth. J. Plant Path.) 67, 69–256 (1961).

ZADOKS, J. C.: Systems analysis and the dynamics of epidemics. Phytopathology 61, 600–610 (1971).

ZADOKS, J. C.: Methodology of epidemiological research. Ann. Rev. Phytopathol. 10, 253–276 (1972).

Chapter II

Automatic Data Processing in Analyses of Epidemics

M. Mogk

1. Introduction

Modern epidemiology is regarded more and more as a subject that derives great benefit from applied mathematics. Only in this respect and not necessarily as a consequence of this, but as a useful procedure as well, automatic data processing and analysis is becoming more and more widely accepted as an advantageous technique in epidemiology.

For quite some time already, epidemiologists have attempted to formulate and solve their problems by mathematical reasoning and to derive descriptive models of a disease or special features thereof. Although quite an amazing number of mathematical models have been proposed for the quantification of "disease" (Kranz, Tables 1–8), there are, however, relatively few of general applicability that on further reflection may be used as routine procedures in automatic data processing (ADP). Some of the mathematical models, such as Van der Plank's apparent infection rate, could be incorporated in a computer program and tested for their epidemiological relevancy on appropriate sets of new data. These generally accepted parameters for the description of disease thus could expediently be compared to the parameters of similar models.

Since our first draft of the holistic approach was developed in 1967, the goals and methods in the analysis of epidemics have changed (Kranz and Mogk, 1971). The first experiences with a new kind of modeling (Waggoner and Horsfall, 1969; Waggoner et al., 1972; Kranz et al., 1973) which is considered to be more meaningful from the biological point of view, basically confirmed the significance of this simulation and new approach in analysis of epidemics. It is accomplished by extensive field observations and detailed experiments in the laboratory from both of which new approaches to a comprehensive understanding of epidemiological processes are rendered possible. According to these findings a different experimental design is required. Ecological data on elements, structures, and events of the disease triangle have to be collected in field trials and growth cabinets. Because of the complexity of interrelations of causative effects in epidemics (Fig. 8), the experimenters are very often faced with the task of collecting huge quantities of data, which they then have to disentangle to test hypotheses. These quantitative studies are undertaken on such a large scale that they inevitably require the use of a computer.

The purpose of this contribution is to outline with some examples the wide array of computerized problems that an epidemiologist might make use of and to demonstrate some of the relevant methods of data processing and analysis, before

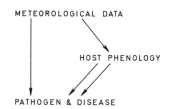

Fig. 8. Abstract system of plant diseases

linear and nonlinear analyses and finally modeling and simulation are treated by my co-authors.

We feel that we cannot here give an inventory of useful procedures. This will have to be left for the time to come when all the claims have been staked and carefully prospected. The emphasis is put much more on the analysis of the raw data by efficient techniques of ADP. These techniques have become automatic procedures, once they have been properly programed. However, they are based on conventional methods of statistics and graphical analyses, which replace pencil and paper methods.

Data processing is dependent on detailed planning and organizing of the experimental layout. The epidemiologist's final aim and objective to accept or to reject hypotheses, is only feasible if data have been collected carefully and systematically and according to the prerequisites of routine programs. I am thus dealing with the steps between planning the experiments and analysis, with subsequent modeling.

2. What Kind of Experiments in Quantitative Epidemiology?

KRANZ (1972), (see also p. 11) suggested that the holistic approach to a quantification of disease and its causative biological and environmental effects would invariably lead to a better understanding and a new basic conception of a model epidemic. The holistic approach provides large amounts of quantitative data. These are obtained from specially designed field experiments which take into consideration the various elements of host, pathogen, and environment as well as control measures.

An attempt to analyze a system of this kind has to be conducted over rather a long period of time and it inevitably requires a large number of accurate measurements. With the set of data obtained it is intended to test as many relevant or epidemiologically meaningful constellations between environment, host, and pathogen/disease as possible, each with a sufficiently high number of replicates and/or events.

The investigation on the epidemic of coffee berry disease (*Colletotrichum coffeanum* Noack) in Kenya (MOGK, 1973), which I studied there for two years in the field, will guide us as an example through the stages of planning the experiment and analyzing the data.

In this study, the experimental units measured consisted of the nodes and internodes of marked branches chosen from coffee trees at random. These units also included the coffee berries and leaves concerned (Fig. 9). Their properties regarding disease and inoculum were under regular observation. According to a rotating

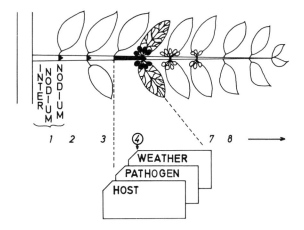

Fig. 9. The units of observation

schedule which was repeated week by week the units of a set of marked branches were evaluated daily.

The appropriate time intervals at which the measurements have to be carried out depend on the rate of increase of the disease, but generally weekly periods of measurement are suitable for most epidemics. For a detailed determination of e.g. the incubation period, more frequent observations are needed.

Which unities of the host have to be chosen for quantitative studies depends largely on the type of plant and on the features of the disease. It can therefore be a leaf, a fruit, a branch or the plant as a whole. The functions of plant growth and phenological development are deducible from the relevant measured features of the host, when time is included as a variable.

Besides the meteorological factors the environmental factors might comprise fungicidal action, nutritional effects (STEINER, 1973) or any non-meteorological properties of the habitat. Here, we may include spatial aspects e.g. tree height or direction of the compass. By experimental design, this group of factors is usually assumed as fixed.

The meteorological factors, *per se,* are interrelated and vary with time and space. The choice of the specific variables to be measured is therefore of crucial importance. In the case of spore germination, for example, the leaf wetness period is often more relevant than the relative air humidity at standard conditions.

Here we do not want to engage in experimental designs, although they certainly have their own features in quantitative epidemiology. The size of a sample may not only be dependent on the variability of the diseased proportion of the plant, but on the difference in uniformity between sampled units of the plants as well. A small crop of coffee berries at every node, which, for example, has been thinned at an advanced stage of the epidemic, may require an increased number of sampled units.

Only some general remarks need be made about the variables under investigation. The variables should be quantifiable by a physical unit of measure. In other cases frequencies of defined events or properties are counted. A list of selected

Table 9. Selected variables from an epidemiological study on coffee berry disease

Meteorological variables (by hours):
  Temperature (°C)
  Relative humidity (%)
  Quantity of rainfall (mm/h)
  Duration or rainfall (min/h)
  Duration os sunshine (min/h)
  Duration of leaf/berry surface wetness (min/h)

Phenological variables:
  Branch:
    Length (cm)
    Position
    Exposure
    Direction
    Stages of bark development
  Coffee berries:
    Number of berries in a node
    Development of berries:
      Age of berries (weeks after flowering)
      Major diameter of berry (mm)
      Weight of 100 berries (g)
      Volume of 100 berries (cm^3)
      Relative dry matter (%)
Variables on disease and inoculum:
  Date of first symptoms appearing
  Number of diseased berries
    Number of mummified berries
  Number of lesions
    Number of active lesions
    Number of scab lesions
  Diseased surface of berries in a node (%)
  Amount of sporulation on berries (number of conidia/cm^2)
  Amount of sporulation on bark (number of conidia/cm^2)

variables from the investigations on coffee berry disease is given for illustration (Table 9). Further variables as, for example, the number of hours with relative humidity above 90% can be defined at the stage of data processing and analysis.

3. What Kind of Questionnaire for Field Experiments?

As early as at the stage of planning the experiments, we have to prepare schedule forms and devise questionnaires with key headings (Fig. 10), which identify the various columns with the information they represent.

The FORTRAN coding sheets of 80 columns together with a key have been used for some years in our field work and proved to be rather convenient (Fig. 11). A set of adjacent columns used to record one item of information, for instance any one item such as number of lesions on a leaf, size of lesions etc., is called a field. The

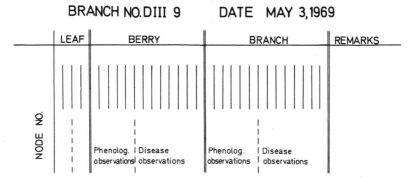

Fig. 10. Example of an observation form for coffee berry disease

dimensions of data fields on coding forms have to be known beforehand. Such a procedure as the use of coding forms saves the costly operation of transferring data from field record forms onto coding sheets which is apparently a source of annoying mistakes.

After the data have been punched, every record, i.e. punchcard, can be individually distinguished by an identification number which may comprise the group of data number, date, treatment, plot, plant or branch number or whatever applies to distinguish separate unities of observation. The entries may be continued on continuation cards.

The most appropriate code must be chosen for each data card. There are three very suitable coding techniques:

1. Sequence codes,
2. Group classification codes,
3. Block codes.

The block codes were the most suited to our purposes, because they combine the advantages of group classification and sequence codes. Within a sub-group (branch) of the set of observations the node numbers of the branch are sequentially arranged.

At this stage, some of the advantages of ADP already seem to be obvious. What is less easily grasped is that these advantages can only be gained if the preparatory work is done well.

4. Automatic Data Acquisition Systems

In quantitative epidemiology the holistic approach (see KRANZ, Section 2.1) requires as many simultaneous measurements as possible. To cope with this, modern technology provided digitisers for automatic data acquisition. For data acquisition of the environmental factors, automatic logging of data has made some progress in meteorology and agricultural meteorology. Since the advance in technology and electronics, various kinds of sensors and the digitizer have been developed, which cope with the demand for high accuracy and efficiency.

These data acquisition systems can be used as off-line recording devices or on-line connections to a computer. If used off-line, they pass the data on to either an

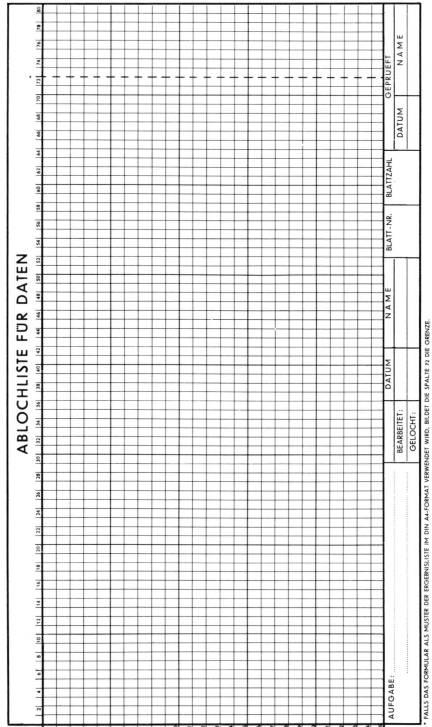

Fig. 11. A FORTRAN coding form

analog display unit, a teletypewriter, a paper tape punch or card punch unit for intermediate display or storage. Used on-line to a computer the data can be processed immediately and the system which is measured can be fed back or controlled.

These systems are not only used in agricultural meteorology and in the environmental control of growth cabinets, but the field of application for analog-to-digital conversion extends to automatic evaluation of photographs and charts. Thus, they provide the answer to some of the widely varying requirements encountered in converting graphical or pictorial information into digital form for computer input. The evaluation of infrared photographs, a method used in estimating the amount of disease, has to be mentioned here.

For measuring the disease, up to now only approximative methods such as the estimation of leaf areas by regression equations (ANALYTIS et al., 1971), or rather cumbersome methods such as planimetry have been available, but they satisfied our purposes only to a limited extent.

A modular digitizer with automated drafting equipment can fill this gap. The digitising system basically consists of a drawing reader, a logic or control unit, and an output device. The samples of diseased leaves which are to be measured are placed on the drawing reader. Then, as the graticule is moved along the contours of the leaf and the outlines of the spots of disease, the registers are automatically updated to give a continuous indication of graticule position. The x and y coordinates are punched on paper tape and used as an input for the program of integrating calculation of leaf area and disease ratio. This system is flexible enough to provide an easy and efficient means of converting any graphical data into digital form for computer analysis. It could be applied as well to the evaluation of all kinds of meteorological recording charts with any time intervals given provided that one can supply the appropriate software for data processing.

5. What Kind of Data?

Most of the data collected are measurements of variables which describe the host and the disease quantitatively. If this is not the case, the frequencies of well-defined qualitative events or properties are counted. In some studies, data gathering may be simplified by assessing estimated values, for example on the rate of disease. Particular model scales for rating have been developed, which allow classification of the amount of disease in a percentage scale ranging from 0.1 to 100%.

Arriving at just this point we have to ask the question about the kind of data and the information so far obtained. From such a vast and confused amount of data there is certainly no information at hand from which further conclusions could be drawn. The important part of some advance in epidemiology, however, lies in the discovery of empirical generalizations which epitomize masses of individual observations.

The amount of data accumulated in two years' observations on coffee berry disease in Kenya can easily be shown by the estimation in Table 10. The data on the variables measured were obtained at regular intervals, the length of which has to take account of relevant changes of the variables.

Table 10. An estimation of items of information from the study on coffee berry disease

Meteorological data:	
hourly records:	
6 variables × 24 hours × 30 days × 9 months × 2 years	77 800 items
daily records:	
8 variables × 30 days × 9 months × 2 years	4 300 items
subtotal	82 100 items
Disease data:	
27 variables × 4 observations/month × 9 months × 18 branches	
× 10 fruiting nodes × 6 fruiting cycles	1 049 800 items
Host data:	
observations done only once:	
4 variables × 18 branches × 6 fruiting cycles	400 items
observations every three weeks:	
5 variables × 13 observations/fruiting cycle × 18 branches × 22	
nodes × 6 fruiting cycles	154 400 items
weekly observations:	
16 variables × 4 weeks × 9 months × 18 branches × 22 nodes	
× 6 fruiting cycles	1 363 600 items
subtotal	1 523 400 items
total	2 655 300 items

Table 11. An estimation of the amount of punch cards from the study on coffee berry disease

Meteorological data:	
750 days of observation × 4 cards per day	3 000 punchcards
Disease data:	
8 nodes (average) × 72 branches × 35 weeks of observation	
× 2 years	40 320 punchcards
Phenological data:	
22 nodes (average) × 72 branches × 35 weeks of observation	
× 2 years	110 680 punchcards
Total	154 000 punchcards

In order to calculate the costs of the preparation of the data carriers, the number of records or punchcards can be estimated correspondingly (Table 11). The data fields of the meteorological data filled four punchcards of 80 columns including the field for the code of data, one day of 24-hourly observations being the unit set of data. With the disease data and phenological data, the former comprised the observations done per node of the branch. The number of data fields on host and disease respectively were 25 and 27 in one punchcard.

It is not uncommon for an experiment to be upset by accidental factors outside the scope of the experiment itself. Under such disadvantageous circumstances, induced for instance by broken instruments, missing replicates or unforeseen events, a systematically composed and complete set of data cannot be achieved. Sections of corrupt data have to be removed by the one who performed the experiment. Generally this implies alternative statistical treatments of the data or the substitution of a few missing or useless items by the application of missing data rules.

More often, however, mistakes arise due to human error when the data are recorded in the field or later on by mispunching. In some cases such errors may be detected, in other cases they may not be distinguishable from the reliable data or may be confused with the so-called outliers. These latter, however, may represent biologically meaningful events which have occurred under certain circumstances beyond our control and for which an explanation is still lacking.

Taking this into account, at the stage of error checking an exacting record filing system will already be quite useful. The card sorter can split up conveniently large sets of data into small distinct groups according to their keynumbers (Fig. 12). Before the rearranged data are further processed, these groups of data can easily be followed up for error detection. The listings of every input should be carefully checked for mispunching and cases that might violate the restrictions of certain Fortran and arithmetical operations.

Although it might be more sophisticated to have the data-sorting part done by the computer, this is not recommended in every case because of its comparatively slow performance. Therefore, sorting from magnetic tape or faster units such as magnetic discs or in core memory might be too costly for large amounts of data. In certain cases only batch processing may be feasible.

On the software side also only a few possibilities have so far been realized for retrieval of extensive and complex data. Software systems which provide a flexible and dynamic data storage and retrieval are not yet generally available. As a consequence of this, for almost every step of data processing, data have to be rearranged or split up into groups for batch processing in order to provide the required input for the available library package programs.

6. How to Reduce the Data?

Automatic data processing comprises by definition not more than the simplest types of record-keeping and handling of information. Basically this means nothing else but collecting source media which contain data or elements of information under some kind of filing system and the handling of such items according to precise rules of procedure. Recording, classifying, sorting, tabulating, calculating, and summarizing items of information is a convenience for all the further methods of analysis. The second step is generally termed data description and reduction. In this step only basic statistical methods are involved, if any at all. Here we will not enter into the particulars of statistics. In Fig. 13 a schematic outline on selected elementary procedures of data processing in quantitative and comparative epidemiology is given.

Recording, sorting and tabulating of data are closely connected processes. The tabular presentation of sorted data makes data more concise and self-explanatory, depending only on the logical arrangement of items. In the process of analysis, data

64 M. MOGK:

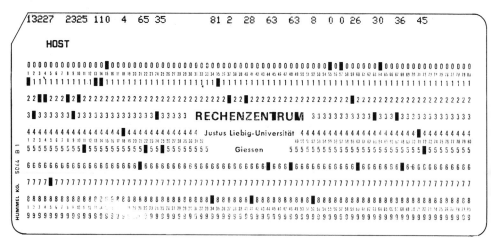

Fig. 12. Punch cards of the three groups of data: weather, pathogen, and host

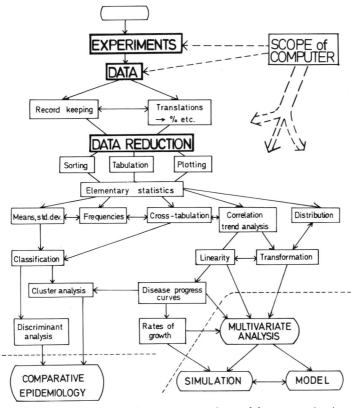

Fig. 13. Schematic outline on selected elementary procedures of data processing in quantitative and comparative epidemiology

must be classified into useful and logical categories. Generally there are four important bases of classification of statistical data: qualitative, quantitative, chronological, and geographical. These classifications already imply the subsequent methods of data analysis. The qualitative differentiation of data may be further summarized by tabulation of frequencies. When items vary in respect to some measurable characteristics, a quantitative classification is appropriate. The quantitative data are put into classes and thus form frequency distributions. The chronological arrangement of data, for example, may lead to the analysis of time series. With geographical distributions, which are treated in most cases as a form of distinct classification, populations of different localities, for example, are made comparable.

The Figs. 14 and 15 demonstrate how the use of rows and columns facilitate comparisons. The table has been subdivided into various parts and labeled for identification in the first column. Skipping a line every five rows is very helpful for the eye to follow the rows across the table. The complete listing comprises some thousand lines of phenological data from twenty years of observations at ten localities. The first cut presents part of the original data whereas in Fig. 15 the table has been re-arranged for the ten stations. Using the first presentation, only comparisons

10131	46	-0	45	-0	49	-0	-0	-0	39	46	38	-0	61	-0	-0	-0	-0	-0	-0	-0	-0	46.28
30131	36	-0	-0	-0	45	-0	-0	-0	-0	-0	-0	-0	-0	-0	-0	-0	-0	-0	-0	-0	-0	40.50
41131	-0	-0	-0	-0	28	50	-0	60	35	-0	-0	-0	-0	63	-0	-0	-0	68	-0	-0	-0	50.66
60131	42	-0	40	-0	42	44	57	55	45	49	46	-0	73	32	-0	54	-0	54	44	16	45	46.12
90131	41	-0	75	-0	-0	-0	67	59	-0	68	-0	-0	-0	-0	-0	-0	-0	-0	-0	-0	-0	62.00
100131	41	-0	45	-0	42	44	63	53	40	48	40	-0	47	-0	-0	-0	-0	-0	-0	-0	-0	46.30
110131	40	-0	46	-0	-0	43	62	-0	48	46	73	-0	52	52	-0	-0	-0	48	47	28	41	48.15
160131	-0	-0	-0	-0	-0	-0	-0	-0	-0	-0	-0	-0	58	-0	-0	-0	-0	56	-0	-0	-0	57.00
210131	-0	-0	-0	-0	-0	-0	-0	-0	-0	-0	-0	-0	61	74	-0	85	-0	63	58	27	63	61.57
230131	-0	-0	-0	-0	42	-0	-0	-0	-0	-0	-0	-0	-0	-0	-0	-0	-0	-0	-0	-0	-0	42.00
10141	19	-0	33	-0	23	33	38	51	24	41	36	-0	46	-0	-0	-0	-0	-0	-0	-0	-0	34.40
30141	22	-0	37	-0	24	-0	-0	-0	-0	-0	-0	-0	-0	-0	-0	-0	-0	-0	-0	-0	-0	27.66
41141	-0	-0	-0	-0	-0	35	26	36	18	41	-0	-0	41	24	-0	-0	-0	24	-6	-0	-0	26.55
60141	30	-0	31	-0	30	36	57	45	34	40	35	-0	47	31	-0	48	-0	31	33	2	34	35.25
90141	24	-0	27	-0	21	27	41	44	30	37	42	-0	-0	-0	-0	-0	-0	-0	-0	-0	-0	32.55
100141	19	-0	27	-0	16	31	40	35	24	36	23	-0	-0	14	-0	71	-0	-0	-0	-0	-0	30.54
110141	22	-0	25	-0	31	33	49	-0	34	38	36	-0	45	28	-0	46	-0	33	31	0	31	32.13
160141	-0	-0	-0	-0	-0	-0	-0	-0	-0	-0	-0	-0	33	28	-0	40	-0	27	22	4	33	26.71
210141	-0	-0	-0	-0	-0	-0	-0	-0	-0	-0	-0	-0	59	-0	-0	41	-0	67	49	22	62	50.00
230141	17	-0	-0	-0	-0	35	39	41	37	37	35	-0	42	30	-0	38	-0	24	-0	-0	-0	34.09
10151	69	-0	-0	-0	62	-0	-0	79	77	-0	90	-0	87	-0	-0	-0	-0	-0	-0	-0	-0	77.33
30151	77	-0	83	-0	-0	-0	-0	-0	-0	-0	-0	-0	-0	-0	-0	-0	-0	-0	-0	-0	-0	80.00
41151	-0	-0	-0	-0	81	-0	-0	70	-0	82	-0	-0	86	67	-0	94	-0	67	63	32	69	71.10
60151	65	-0	81	-0	69	77	104	81	88	85	78	-0	83	65	-0	82	-0	76	64	35	67	75.00
90151	64	-0	82	-0	60	-0	102	79	76	80	74	-0	-0	-0	-0	-0	-0	-0	-0	-0	-0	77.12
100151	66	-0	79	-0	86	70	96	86	77	87	77	-0	78	75	-0	79	-0	-0	-0	-0	-0	79.66
110151	87	-0	79	-0	73	-0	103	81	-0	91	85	-0	83	68	-0	90	-0	73	66	29	69	76.92
160151	-0	-0	-0	-0	-0	-0	-0	-0	-0	-0	-0	-0	79	65	-0	71	-0	67	61	33	65	63.00
210151	-0	-0	-0	-0	-0	-0	-0	-0	-0	-0	-0	-0	90	72	-0	85	-0	87	81	48	67	75.71
230151	63	-0	78	-0	67	80	98	82	76	87	79	-0	80	66	-0	80	-0	66	-0	-0	-0	77.07

Fig. 14. Sorted reference table for comparison of phenological events and disease occurrence

6013	129	117	127	135	135	141	123	136	123	129	115	138	123	143	140	122	130	118	132	139	126	129.57
60131	42	0	40	0	42	44	57	55	45	49	46	0	73	32	0	54	0	54	44	16	45	46.12
60132	27	36	67	26	29	15	51	23	53	21	35	36	51	26	36	52	38	27	31	19	34	34.90
60133	37	21	0	0	0	44	31	66	34	35	23	28	33	63	9	64	70	47	61	67	24	42	42.05
60134	0	0	0	0	0	0	0	122	92	89	164	120	109	0	75	76	97	89	74	110	0	101.41
6014	141	129	136	137	147	149	123	146	134	138	126	149	149	144	148	128	143	141	143	153	137	140.04
60141	30	0	31	0	30	36	57	45	34	40	35	0	47	31	0	48	0	31	33	2	34	35.25
60142	15	24	58	24	17	7	51	13	42	12	24	25	25	25	28	46	25	4	20	5	23	24.42
60143	25	9	0	0	32	23	66	24	24	14	17	22	37	8	56	64	34	38	56	10	31	31.05
60144	0	0	0	0	0	0	0	112	81	80	153	109	83	0	67	70	84	66	63	96	0	88.66
6015	106	104	86	100	108	108	76	110	80	93	83	111	113	110	100	94	87	96	112	120	104	100.04
60151	65	0	81	0	69	77	104	81	88	85	78	0	83	65	0	82	0	76	64	35	67	75.00
60152	50	49	108	61	56	48	98	49	96	57	67	63	61	59	76	80	81	49	51	38	56	64.42
60153	60	34	0	0	71	64	113	60	78	59	60	60	73	42	104	98	90	83	87	43	64	70.68
60154	0	0	0	0	0	0	0	148	135	125	196	147	119	0	115	104	140	111	94	129	0	130.25
6016	101	105	88	-0	106	98	85	108	98	85	87	112	108	112	110	92	94	103	115	118	103	101.40
60161	70	0	79	0	71	87	95	83	70	93	74	0	88	63	0	84	0	69	61	37	68	74.50
60162	55	48	106	0	58	58	89	51	78	65	63	62	66	57	66	82	74	42	48	40	57	63.25
60163	65	33	0	0	73	74	104	62	60	67	56	59	78	40	94	100	83	76	84	45	65	69.36
60164	0	0	0	0	0	0	0	150	117	133	192	146	124	0	105	106	133	104	91	131	0	127.40
6017	94	-0	84	87	98	92	78	98	84	75	72	108	106	98	114	77	75	96	93	90	84	90.15
60171	77	0	83	0	79	93	102	93	84	103	89	0	90	77	0	99	0	76	83	65	87	86.25
60172	62	0	110	74	66	64	96	61	92	75	78	66	68	71	62	97	93	49	70	68	76	74.90
60173	72	0	0	0	81	80	111	72	74	77	71	63	80	54	90	115	102	83	106	73	84	82.66
60174	0	0	0	0	0	0	0	160	131	143	207	150	126	0	101	121	152	111	113	159	0	139.50

Fig. 15. Sorted reference table on phenological data of 10 localities under observation for 21 years

of the years were feasible, whereas the second facilitated further conclusions on the variability of the stations. If the data are complete, every sub-table arranged in such a way can be used as an input for a program of analysis of variance between years and locations and further comparative studies. These very extensive tables, covering many pages, are called general or reference tables and serve as a repository of information.

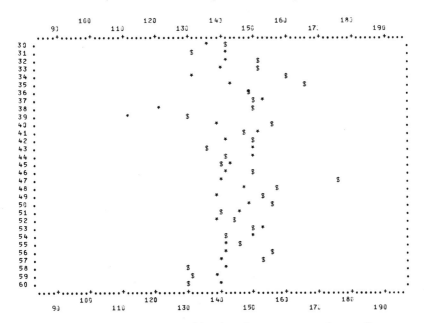

Fig. 16. Original data of two variables plotted against time on the coordinate

A method equivalent to the presentation of reference tables is the graphic presentation of original data, which is effective for a limited amount of information (Fig. 16). If the data imply a curve, the output may be very distinct. In Fig. 16 two temperatures, measured at different times of the day, are plotted for comparison.

Many research workers who wish to see their data or results in graphical form plot them by hand, which may demand great skill and accuracy. This is provided by the automatic plotter (Fig. 17), which in certain cases may provide the final form of presentation of results. Such plots can be produced in different scales and colors.

A summary table is invariably the result of boiling down information contained in one or more reference tables. This will lead us to problems of elementary statistics or data description. At this output level we encounter some of the most frequently used methods of data reduction. One method of summarizing statistical data consists in the formation of a frequency distribution and the calculation of its parameters. In this device the various items of a series of measurements are classified into groups and the number of items falling into each group is stated.

The computer printer can provide a graphical output of the results in form of a histogram (Fig. 18), or a curve diagram of frequencies.

In experimental epidemiology normal distributions are only encountered with certain data, but they may correspond to one or the other of the commonly used theoretical distributions of mathematical statistics. If such a correspondence can be established, the theoretical distribution can serve as a model. The parameters which define the theoretical distribution summarize the properties of the empirical data approximatively. The attributes of a frequency distribution can be characterized by three measures of central tendency: the arithmetic mean, the median, and the

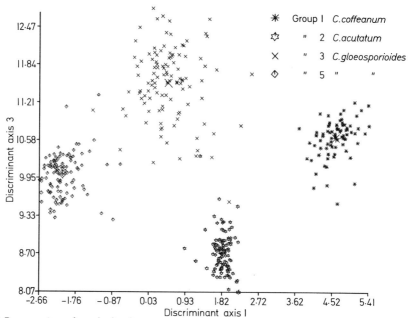

Fig. 17. Presentation of results by the automatic plotter, from a taxonomic study on *Colletotrichum coffeanum*

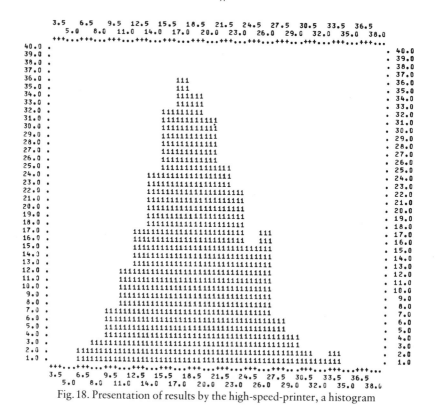

Fig. 18. Presentation of results by the high-speed-printer, a histogram

mode. The measures of dispersion, skewness, and kurtosis describe the divergence from a normal distribution.

In this connection we would like to refer to transformation of data, which may be employed to approximate a theoretical distribution. In most cases the normal distribution is advantageous for further statistical treatment of the data. The transformations of disease progress curves will be taken up later in this chapter. (For a more detailed discussion see KRANZ, 4.2.

Cross-tabulation is another method that is very useful in the analysis of biological events. Such a program computes two-way frequency tables of the data put in. Thus they may represent a final form of reporting. Let us assume that we want to analyze the frequencies of coincident events of relative humidity and temperature in successive hourly intervals and defined ranges of measurement. If we take into consideration that relative humidity and temperature are somehow correlated, such a graphical tabulation may be a first approach to problems of correlation and demonstrate clearly the structure of the data. From the two-dimensional plot of the distribution "outliers" can be checked for errors. With some correlation programs the output provides one-page cross-tabulation plots of any two variables, which demonstrate the kind of relation graphically (Fig. 19).

In theory, cross-tabulation could be extended to a problem in multiple space. Depending on the number of variables involved, and on the number of classes for the classification of the events, this procedure will yield an enormous number of possible combinations. However, not all of the frequencies of coincident events will be of interest for further analysis by the epidemiologist.

If we assume that only those frequency classes, let us say, of temperature, relative humidity, and leaf wetness around the optimum conditions for fungal growth and development are of relevant importance for certain epidemiological processes, we may then confine the analysis of frequencies only to such coincident events.

The program COINCIDENCE (MOGK, 1973) which was written in Fortran for these purposes is applied to illuminate the hypotheses on the interrelated meteorological factors. Data on spore trapping or sporulation, for example, can be included for different aims. It has been constructed by making use of the Fortran IF-statement together with logical and comparative operators such as .LT., .LE., .EQ., .NE., .AND., .OR., etc. An example of this essential part of the program COINCIDENCE is shown in Fig. 20.

The long list output of COINCIDENCE tabulates the original meteorological data for 24 h in every day for easy comparison. If a coincident event occurs that suits the defined conditions, the data field is marked by stars. This means, for example, that during this time interval the meteorological conditions might have been favorable for spore germination. The reference table is summarized weekly and gives an account of the frequencies. Different tests with other combinations of intervals can be run successively. Furthermore we have provided with this program an optional output that summarizes the coincident events, marked by a star, in a graphical table (Fig. 21). Here the coincident events of four meteorological variables with temperature intervals around the optimum temperature of $21°$ C for conidia germination of *Colletotrichum coffeanum* are counted.

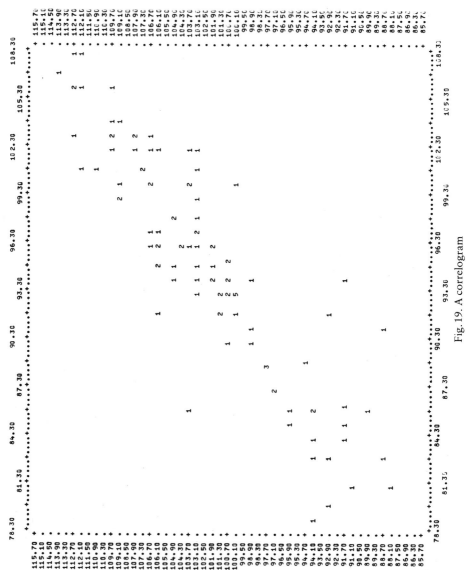

Fig. 19. A correlogram

```
C     *** VERARBEITUNG ***
      DO 100  J = 1, IL
      DO  90  I = 1, IVA
      IF (ART(I)) GO TO 70
      IF (WERT(I,J) .NE. UG(I)) ERG(J) = .FALSE.
      GO TO 80
   70 IF (WERT(I,J) .LT. UG(I) .OR. OG(I) .LE. WERT(I,J))
    * ERG(J) = .FALSE.
   80 CONTINUE
      IF (.NOT. ERG(J) GO TO 100
   90 CONTINUE
  100 CONTINUE
```

Fig. 20. The *IF*-statement and logical or comparative operators applied to the principal part of the program COINCIDENCE

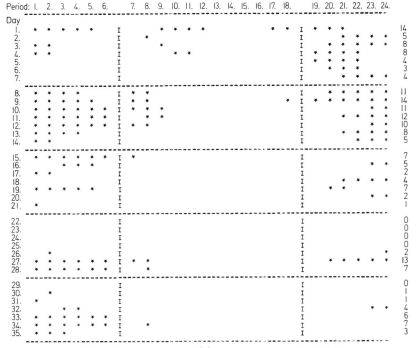

Fig. 21. Summary output of the program COINCIDENCE

All these methods of inventory of data yield useful tabulations and more than that, they provide plots which facilitate the verification and the interpretation of the data.

Simple correlation problems are relatively easily mastered, whereas the analysis of time-series, a too-common problem in epidemiology, is not so easy to tackle. One of the current procedures for correlating the fluctuations of two time-series consists of determining the partial correlation existing between the two series when time is held constant. This adjustment of data with time as a third variable is called trend analysis.

With the kind of raw data that we normally obtain from field observations a considerable amount of editing and screening of the basic information is required before the more elaborate analyses can be carried out. Some of the pertinent methods have already been mentioned. Most of the generally applicable, but more complicated statistical programs, require further prerequisites. Some programs can only be applied on condition that no observations are missing. This is rarely the case with biological data. Various assumptions are made also about the data in the statistical models associated with these analyses. The examination of data characteristics appropriate to these assumptions can be assisted with all the programs mentioned for data description and reduction.

Now that we have given examples to cover some of the programs of the output level which were of a generally descriptive nature, we now proceed to the test level. On this level we are mostly concerned with linearity and normality of the data. It is essential to achieve at least an approximation of both these prerequisites for linear models of multivariate analysis.

There are some excellent computer programs for tests of linearity and normality which might already give a hint as to what transformations are the most suitable. To straighten the asymmetrical disease progress curves, however, is generally more complex, as they tend to behave like complicated growth curves. Therefore we can suggest that the derivates of the growth curves as shown by Gompertz, Mitscherlich, and Bertalanffy are those most suited to straightening the various types of disease progress curves at least approximatively. This approach has been successfully employed by ANALYTIS (1973) for apple scab as a beginning (Table 3).

The parameters of disease progress curves and the rate of growth may be the final result of an analysis. How these results provide useful parameters for modeling and simulation will be taken up by Waggoner.

After some of the more common trends of data analyzing have been demonstrated, we will now proceed to a field of data analyzing that can be employed in comparative epidemiology (p. 47). It is termed classification of quantitative and qualitative information and is applied to the study of groups or populations. These methods comprise many mathematically quite distinct forms of cluster analyses and discriminant analyses, all including the techniques of multivariate analyses.

Cluster analyses may suffer from the shortcoming of giving no clear indication of what really determines a cluster. It is perhaps worth pointing out that clustering often imposes an hierarchical structure on a sample by the comparison of pairs of characters. Before cluster analyses are employed as a method of classification we have to consider whether the results will be more significant from the biological point of view or not if, for example, weights are applied.

The program CLUS, for example, has several criteria for testing a meaningful separation of clusters. KRANZ and LÖRINCZ (1970) employed this method of cluster analysis in their comparative study on disease progress curves and thus separated a set of curves of epidemics into several assemblages or clusters on the basis of a set of attributes which they share. Their results demonstrated that from this point of view not every epidemic has a disease progress curve of its own, as Van der Plank claims. These findings are biologically significant as can easily be shown.

Classification and identification is very important in numerical taxonomy of parasitic organisms as well as of closely related varieties of the host. By means of the multiple discriminant analysis it is possible to identify taxonomically distinct groups by qualitative and quantitative features of the items. Although this technique has already been worked out by R. A. FISHER in 1936, its application, however, is increasing since computer programs have become generally available for it.

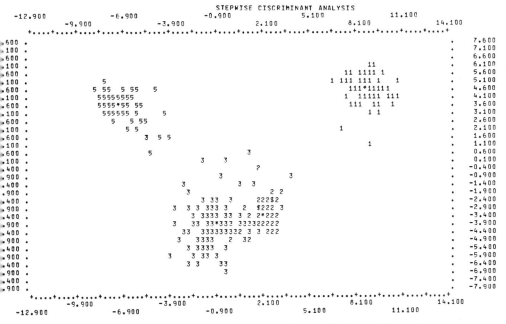

Fig. 22. Graphical output of the stepwise discriminant analysis applied to problems of comparative epidemiology

The discriminant analysis operates stepwise and constructs for every step a multiple discriminant function including one more variable. By this procedure it is possible to select from a relatively large amount of variables that combination which provides an optimum selectivity. For further problems of classification only these features are of relevant importance. Transformations of the raw data may be useful for the optimisation of the effectiveness of the discriminant function.

HINDORF (1973) in his population study of the genus *Colletotrichum* separated three species of *Colletotrichum* with a high probability on the basis of morphological characters (Figs. 17 and 22).

The same procedure also allows the classification of individuals of unknown samples. These individuals are assigned to one or other of the groups with the least chance of being misclassified. In addition to this, canonical variables can be computed and the first three can be plotted to give an optimal three-dimensional picture of the identification. The discriminant analysis is, thus, an important method for unbiased decision in classification for the reasons demonstrated.

7. Computer Programing and Availability of Software

As we have seen, the general statistical and mathematical techniques of data evaluation are a wide field for the use of data processing systems in epidemiology. The software for the techniques of data reduction and analysis are available at almost

Table 12. Some selected programs compiled from DAVIES (1971) (1), DIXON (1970) (2), and VELDMAN (1967) (3)

Sorting, tabulation an plotting of raw data:
    Sorting an array in ascending and/or descending order (1)
    Ranking an array of numbers (1)
    Tabulation of frequency tables (1)

Description of data:
    Data summarizing programs (1)
    Simple data description *BMD* 01 *D* (2)
    General plot of data including histogram *BMD* 05 *D* (2)

Correlation and regression analysis:
    Correlation with transgeneration *BMD* 02 *D* (2)
    Auto-correlations in time-series (1)
    Cross-correlations in time-series (1)
    Auto- and cross-lag intercorrelation (3)
    Stepwise regression *BMD* 02 *R* (2)

Fitting theoretical distributions to data:
    Fitting a normal distribution and testing goodness of fit (1)
    Fitting a Poisson distribution and testing goodness of fit (1)
    Fitting a binomial distribution and testing goodness of fit (1)
    Fitting a negative binomial distribution and testing goodness of fit (1)

Classification:
    Cluster analysis (1)
    Hierarchical grouping analysis (3)
    Stepwise discriminant analysis for several groups *BMD* 05 *M* (2)
    Multiple discriminant analysis (1)

---

every computer center in the library of general purpose programs. Generally, a library of general purpose subroutines such as the *SSP* routines is provided.

An extensive body of literature on the use of methods employing electronic data processing is developing in all fields of ecology and other sciences. A brief table of selected programs for general purpose of *ADP* is compiled from DAVIES (1971), DIXON (1970), and VELDMAN (1967) (Table 12). With some of these given examples similar analyses may be achieved. Some of the programs which have been published could easily be adapted or parts of them could serve as subroutines. The adaptation and application of routine programs, however, requires at least a little training in programing computer languages.

From my experience, sufficient skill in constructing programs in Fortran can be acquired with about two weeks of basic practical training. The skill involved in elementary programing is by far easier to learn than the study of higher mathematics or statistics. Furthermore, if a scientist has become a specialist in his field much or all of his considerable training has been in applications, not theoretical mathematical modeling. However, some of the more complex methods of *ADP* need a rather deep insight into the mathematical reasoning involved. It is for this reason that it is of importance to call on a biometrician and an expert programer to take part in interdisciplinary projects.

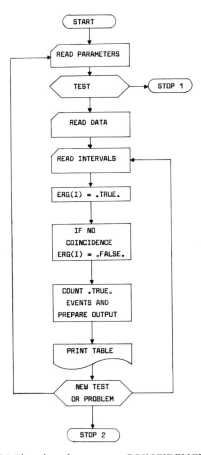

Fig. 23. Flowchart for program COINCIDENCE

Special purpose programs written by the epidemiologist himself may in general be quite simple. However, they may also be of considerable convenience and great efficiency. Some could be handled with a desk calculator if it were not for the massive amount of bookkeeping involved.

The computer will perform its task automatically if it is properly programed. To achieve this, it is necessary to perform two steps. First, whenever a program or method for solution is sought, decisions have to be made about the general type of problem we are dealing with and the form of analysis that appears appropriate, either in the field of data processing or numerical analysis. Second, a general flow-chart must be designed which can be translated into computer language step by step (Fig. 23). After that we are faced with the special task of instructing the computer to carry out the chosen sequence of calculations. This is achieved by means of a suitably designed program of orders.

The so-called *DO*-loop or iteration loop is one of the features contributing to the versatility of the language. It is used for the description of discrete states or time points. By means of the *DO*-loop one of the most powerful aspects of automatic programing can be achieved by which instructions for a long cycle of repetitive operations can be described very simply and compactly. This is one of the special requirements by which the recurrence of time effects in epidemics can be solved approximately if the time intervals *dt* are suitably chosen to allow for quantifiable interferences of the environment. This technique has been applied by WAGGONER and HORSFALL (1969) to the EPIDEM and the successive simulator programs, which are all written in Fortran.

The use of computers has led to a fundamentally new situation: Computations and methods, the employment of which seemed to be inconceivable before, are now made possible by routines. The quantity of the data put into the computer, the increase of precision and the use of new and extensive techniques of computation have led to new dimensions of epidemiological research. But we have not yet reached the stage—nor should we ever reach it—where an "integrated" data processing system could be applied without thought to solve all the problems arising in research and practical applications. Finding the essential bits and pieces in epidemiological research will be left to scientific skill and flashes of inspiration in order to make better experiments, not alone to the routines of a computer.

The computer certainly has many advantages such as speed, accuracy, handling of large volumes, easy storage and retrieval of information as well as the reduction in number of human mistakes by repetitive operations. Thus a computer can replace staff and save skilled people from doing routine work. However, they cannot be released; they will have to be absorbed by carrying out experimental research work and where they may find it even more demanding, collecting the "fine" data which we need.

References

ANALYTIS, S.: Zur Methodik der Analyse von Epidemien, dargestellt am Apfelschorf [*Venturia inaequalis* (Cooke) Aderh.]. Acta Phytomedica 1, 76 pp. (1973).

ANALYTIS, S., KRANZ, J., STUMPF, A.: Eine Methode zur Berechnung der Blattfläche. Angew. Bot. 45, 111–114 (1971).

DAVIES, R. G.: Computer programing in quantitative biology, 492 pp. London and New York: Academic Press 1971.

DIXON, W. J. (Ed.): BMD Biomedical computer programs, 600 pp. Berkeley and Los Angeles: University of California Press 1970.

HINDORF, H.: Qualitative and quantitative Unterschiede in der *Colletotrichum*-Population auf *Coffea arabica* L. in Kenia. 1. Eine Methode zur systematischen Trennung von Pilzpopulationen. Phythopath. Z. 77, 97–106 (1973).

KRANZ, J.: Einige Voraussetzungen für die Planung und Durchführung von Feldversuchen in der Epidemiologie. Z. Pflanzenkrankh. 79, 573–581 (1972).

KRANZ, J.: Bemerkungen zur Simulation von Epidemien. EDV in Medizin und Biologie. 4, 41–45 (1973).

KRANZ, J., LÖRINCZ, D.: Methoden zum automatischen Vergleich epidemischer Abläufe bei Pflanzenkrankheiten. Phytopath. Z. 67, 225–233 (1970).

KRANZ, J., MOGK, M.: Electronic data processing of field experiments on the epidemiology of *Colletotrichum coffeanum*. 2nd Int. Symp. on Plant Pathology, New Delhi (1971).

KRANZ, J., MOGK, M., STUMPF, A.: EPIVEN—ein Simulator für Apfelschorf. Z. Pflanzenkrankh. 80, 181–187 (1973).

MOGK, M.: Untersuchungen zur Epidemiologie von *Colletotrichum coffeanum* Noack sensu Hindorf in Kenia, eine Analyse der Wirt-Parasit-Umwelt-Beziehungen. Ph. D. Thesis. Univ. Gießen (1973).

STEINER, K. G.: Beziehungen zwischen Wirt, Parasit, Witterung und Fungiziden bei der Kaffeekirschenkrankheit (*Colletotrichum coffeanum* Noack). Ph. D. Thesis. Univ. Gießen (1973).

VELDMAN, D. J.: Fortran Programing for the behavioral sciences, 406 pp. New York: Holt, Rinehart and Winston 1967.

WAGGONER, P. E., HORSFALL, J. G.: EPIDEM, a simulator of plant disease written for a computer. Conn. Agr. Exp. Sta. Bull. **698** (1969).

WAGGONER, P. E., HORSFALL, J. G., LUKENS, R. J.: EPIMAY, a simulator of southern corn leaf blight. Conn. Agr. Expt. Sta. Bull. **729** (1972).

CHAPTER III

Multiple Regression Analysis in the Epidemiology of Plant Diseases

D. J. BUTT and D. J. ROYLE

1. Introduction

During the progress in time of an epidemic, cycles of events occur repeatedly in which inoculum is produced, dispersed and intercepted, and some of the surviving propagules infect; as a consequence of this multiplication the disease intensifies and can eventually reduce crop yield. The severity of disease throughout the epidemic is dependent upon a multiplicity of environmental factors, both biological and physical. Figure 24 depicts an epidemic schematically and illustrates the main features which are of interest to the epidemiologist. Mathematical analysis of the whole system or a part of it can lead directly to improvements in disease control.

The ultimate aims of an analysis should be taken into consideration by the epidemiologist at the outset, from his knowledge of the particular disease and the practices used to control it. Thus in certain crops, e.g. cereals, it may be important to evaluate the economic feasibility of applying one or more critically-timed applications of a fungicide. Such a treatment may be acceptable if a potential epidemic can be identified sufficiently early, or if potential crop loss can be estimated in time. In other crops, e.g. fruit, where spray programs are routine, an analysis of the epidemic may suggest the re-timing or omission of some fungicide applications. Where sources of disease resistance are utilized, the performance of resistant genotypes may best be evaluated by analysis of comparative disease development in the field. Moreover, disease control on a resistant variety may benefit from a few applications of well-timed fungicides. These sorts of practical benefits can be achieved from the comparison of epidemics, disease prediction and the quantification of key factors which determine disease severity.

The epidemiologist can adopt schemes of analysis according to his interest in one or more of five features of an epidemic. In the first, interest may focus on the *progress of the epidemic* in time, as represented by the curve AB in Fig. 24. Equations can be derived which describe such progress curves, transformed or otherwise, in order to facilitate the interpretation and comparison of epidemics in the broad terms of, for example, seasonal or geographical weather, varietal resistance or control methods. In addition, and this is necessary for the purpose of forecasting disease, attempts may be made to explain levels of disease or associated measurements such as cumulative spore concentration, reached at successive points along the progress curve (e.g. disease d_2 at time t_2) in terms of factors which occurred previously such as the amount of disease (e.g. d_1), pathogen activity and environmental factors at time t_1. In the second, interest may concentrate on the *rate of*

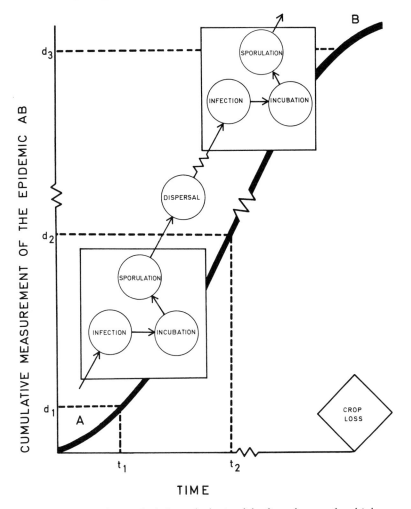

Fig. 24. Features of an epidemic which form the basis of the five schemes of multiple regression analysis described in the text

disease increase, and changes in disease severity as the epidemic progresses are interpreted by analyzing successive changes in disease (e.g. the difference $d_2 - d_1$ in the interval t_1 to t_2) in relation to environmental factors. In the third, the analysis may be concerned with the factors determining the level of *disease severity* reached on one occasion, usually the level of disease at the end of a season (e.g. d_3). In this scheme there is no interest in the rate of disease progress. In the fourth, the epidemiologist's attention may be centered on the *events in the disease cycle* which are related to each other within relatively brief time periods, represented in Fig. 24 by boxes. Thus there may be a desire to analyze infection, incubation, sporulation and dispersal of the pathogen in terms of the environmental factors occurring within these same time periods. Knowledge of the key factors affecting infection and incubation periods may permit short-term warnings of disease behavior, which in practice provides the possibility of day-to-day control tactics such as the post-infection application of fungicide. On a more ambitious scale, knowledge of the relationships of pathogen activity and environmental factors occurring at time t_1, with subsequent events at time t_2, may provide the possibility for longer-term forecasts; broad control strategy can then be determined, including the opportunity of implementing protective spray programs. Finally, the investigator may attempt to evaluate *crop loss*, which is a consequence rather than a part of the epidemic. The analysis may reveal the minimum level of disease which can be tolerated before an economically significant loss in yield results, a particular stage of crop growth when loss may be estimated, or may allow yield to be forecast from disease levels early in the epidemic. A number of relevant examples (some of which are quoted) in this chapter) are given in tables 4–8.

With the growing interest in quantitative methods of analyzing plant diseases it is appropriate to review the role of multiple regression analysis (MRA) in epidemiology. As a technique in epidemiological research MRA has been of considerable interest since the electronic computer became widely available. It is interesting to note that in entomology, MRA has been widely used since COOK (1921) related weather factors to fluctuations in numbers of flying Lepidoptera. Several useful accounts of the method in entomological investigations have been published (ANDREWARTHA and BIRCH, 1954; WATT, 1961; JOHNSON, 1969) and the underlying philosophy is pertinent to its use in plant pathology.

2. The Nature of Multiple Regression Analysis in Epidemiology

If an investigator wishes to explain day-to-day variation in the number of disease lesions per leaf which develop, following a standard incubation, on potted plants exposed to natural infection on successive days, and if this variable is considered to be a function of the spore dose, measured by a spore trap on each exposure day, then regression describes the relationship. The number of lesions is called the dependent (response) variable Y, and is said to regress on the spore dose, called the independent (determining) variable X. The application of regression analysis to joint observations of these variables will evaluate the importance of spore dose as a variable contributing to lesion numbers, and estimate the change in the number of lesions which can be expected from a unit change in spore dose, so providing a possible basis for the prediction of disease severity using spore dose as a predictor. Any varying aspect of an epidemic, such as daily spore concentration, rate of disease increase, or crop loss, can be considered as a dependent variable and regressed on factors like temperature, crop density and age of crop when these are expressed as variables such as daily mean temperature, leaf area index and date of planting, respectively. It will be emphasized later that evidence of a statistical dependence of one variable on another is not proof of causation, although in the example above it would be biologically meaningful to conclude that spore dose is a key (important) variable in the determination of disease severity.

In contrast to regression, correlation measures the degree of association between variables of equal status; there need be no concept of cause and effect. For the calculation of correlation both variables must be normally distributed, whereas

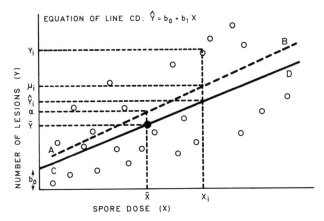

Fig. 25. The relationship between the true regression line (*AB*) and the estimated regression line (*CD*)

for regression this is necessary only for the dependent variable. In writing this section much guidance has been obtained from the books by WILLIAMS (1959), DRAPER and SMITH (1966), SNEDECOR and COCHRAN (1967), and BLISS (1970). We present an account which we hope will give epidemiologists a clear insight into the nature of MRA, and allow a better understanding and application of multiple regression equations.

Figure 25 is a scatter diagram of number of lesions (*Y*) plotted against spore dose (*X*), and shows that in the hypothetical investigation above, a spore dose of X_i spores/cm^2 was associated with the subsequent appearance of Y_i lesions per leaf on the potted plants. We know that variation accompanies the measurement of biological responses to specified treatments, and we attribute this unexplained variation to "error". It is not surprising, therefore, that there is not a single, unique number of lesions associated with any specified spore dose, and according to the theory of regression Y_i is one value in a population of Y values which co-exist at spore dose X_i and are normally distributed about a mean of μ_i lesions. The line *AB* which joins these population means (*μ*) is the *true regression* of lesion numbers on spore dose. Let us assume that the relationship between these two variables can be described by the simple model,

$$Y = \alpha + \beta (X - \bar{X}) + e \tag{1}$$

in which α lesions occur when the spore dose is at its mean, $\bar{X}$. The parameter β is the *true regression coefficient* and the slope of the true regression line *AB*. The error *e* is that random part of the response of the dependent variable Y which is not fixed by the constants α and β, and is the reason for the random dispersal of the observations of Y either side of the true regression line. According to the model [Eq. (1)] the number of lesions is a linear function (*AB* is a straight line) of spore dose, plus the random effect of error which is independent of the spore dose. The role of regression analysis would be to evaluate this proposed model to see if it adequately represents the observed data.

Although the true regression line is represented as *AB* in Fig. 25, its real position and slope are unknown. However, using the method of least squares, the straight line which best fits the available data can be drawn and this is the *estimated regression line*, represented as *CD*. It passes through the mean of each variable and is the line of the regression equation,

$$\hat{Y} = \bar{Y} + b(X - \bar{X}) \tag{2}$$

where $\hat{Y}$ is an estimate of the population mean number of lesions (μ) at any specified spore dose and is therefore the *expected* value of the dependent variable, $\bar{X}$ and $\bar{Y}$ are the means of each variable, and the *regression coefficient b* is the slope of the line *CD*, and is an estimate of the parameter β. Equation (2) is often written in the form of the predictive equation,

$$\hat{Y} = b_0 + b_1(X) \tag{3}$$

in which the constant b_0 ($= \bar{Y} - b\bar{X}$) is called the intercept because when the spore dose is zero, b_0 lesions are predicted. (It is clear from the scatter diagram that in this example the intercept is positive. This anomaly of infections without inoculum is explained by a high detection threshhold of the spore trap). Using Eq. (3) the expected number of lesions (e.g. $\hat{Y}_i$) can be estimated for any level of spore dose (e.g. X_i) within the range of *X*-values used in calculating the constants b_0 and b_1.

This example of simple linear regression, in which the dependent variable regresses on one independent variable, expands into multiple (partial) regression when the number of lesions per leaf is considered to be a linear function of each of two or more independent variables, as in the predictive equation,

$$\hat{Y} = b_0 + b_1X_1 - b_2X_2 - - - - - - + b_nX_n. \tag{4}$$

Constants b_1 to b_n are *partial* regression coefficients, being estimates of the net linear effect of the independent variables X_1 to X_n respectively on the total response of the dependent variable. The partial regression coefficient b_1 is the slope of the linear regression of Y on X_1 when the effects on Y of variables X_2 to X_n have been allowed for. If we introduce atmospheric humidity as a second determining factor in our example, then the bivariate regression equation,

$$\hat{Y} = b_0 + b_1X_1 - b_2X_2 \tag{5}$$

can be interpreted to read that independently of the mean humidity (X_2) on the day of exposure of the potted plants to infection, the severity of disease which subsequently developed increased on average by b_1 lesions for each unit increase of spore dose (X_1), and independently of spore dose, each unit increase of mean humidity lowered the severity of the disease by b_2 lesions. It is this ability to measure the net effect of each independent variable that makes MRA a valuable analytical method in epidemiology.

An additive model of the type represented by Eq. (5) in which the dependent variable is a linear function of each independent variable is unlikely to describe the causative (functional) pathways which relate variables, and may be illogical (for example, see [5.4]). Two points should be noted, however. First, each independent variable need not be expressed as a simple term; SCHRÖDTER and ULLRICH (1965) provide a good example of a multiple regression equation in which each independent variable is a complex term. Second, notwithstanding the linear nature of multiple regression models it is possible to incorporate into them independent variables which accommodate interactions and non-linear responses. Consider wind speed (X_3) as a further determinant of lesion numbers, and the addition of three more variables to Eq. (5) so that it now reads,

$$\hat{Y} = b_0 + b_1 X_1 - b_2 X_2 + b_3 X_3 + b_4 X_1 X_3 + b_5 X_3^2. \tag{6}$$

(By convention, the partial regression coefficients b_4 and b_5 should be written b_{13} and b_{33} respectively).

Variable $X_1 X_3$ will accommodate any interaction between spore dose and wind speed; X_3^2 will accommodate a non-linear component in the gross response of the dependent variable to wind speed. Equation (6) remains an example of linear regression because the dependent variable is regarded as a linear function of each of the five independent variables, irrespective of the form of the latter. In this way a linear model can be fitted to a curved response surface; the total response of the dependent variable is regarded as the sum of linear effects of independent variables expressed to any power, e.g. X_3^2, X_3^3.

Two questions concern the nomenclature and independence of the independent variables. With respect to nomenclature, GOLDBERGER (1964) distinguishes between the regressors, which are the X-variables in the equation, and the independent variables, which can be represented by two or more regressors. In this sense the independent variable wind speed is represented in Eq. (6) by the regressors X_3 and X_3^2. In this paper, however, we shall use independent variable to mean any X-variable.

Need the independent variables be independent of each other? The answer is no. In fact, there is often intercorrelation between the X-variables either because they are intrinsically associated, as between weather factors, or mathematically associated, as between X_3 and X_3^2. Intercorrelations are certainly expected when the variables are records of uncontrolled field experiments producing what has been referred to as "messy" data. A high degree of intercorrelation between independent variables does not prevent the assembly of a good predictive equation with a high R^2 (see below), but the accuracy and statistical significance of the partial regression coefficients may be very low. This problem is discussed in Section 4.

Analysis of variance is an important aspect of MRA because it allows the proposed regression model to be tested and compared with others. The basis of the analysis of variance is that total variation in observed values of the dependent variable, i.e. the total sum of squares (SS) of deviations of Y from their mean $\bar{Y}$ $(= \Sigma y^2)$ is made up of (1) the sum of squares due to the regression, i.e. the SS of deviations of predicted values $\hat{Y}$ from the mean $\bar{Y}$ $(= \Sigma \hat{y}^2)$ plus (2) the residual variation due to error, i.e. the SS of deviations of observed values Y from predicted values $\hat{Y}$. The residual variation, which is evident in the discrepancy between observed and predicted values, is a measure of the inadequacy of the independent variables in the regression equation to account for the total variation in the dependent variable. The mean square (s^2) of the residuals (deviations) is therefore an estimate of the variance of the error term in the model [e in Eq. (1)], and is used in variance ratio (F) tests of the statistical significance of the combined and individual effects of the independent variables. By this procedure regression equations are tested and compared. The standard error s, sometimes expressed $100s/\bar{Y}$, measures the precision of prediction and is used to calculate standard errors of partial regression coefficients and predictions.

The coefficient of multiple determination R^2 is the ratio $\Sigma\hat{y}^2/\Sigma y^2$ and is often expressed as a percentage. This familiar statistic is the proportion of total *variation* in the dependent variable which is accounted for by multiple regression on the independent variables, and is a convenient assessment of the fit (adequacy) of the regression equation since when R^2 is near unity, almost all the variation has been explained. It should be noted that when the dependent variable is expressed as, for example, log Y, the R^2 value can appear deceptively high because it is measuring the accountability of variation in the transformed variable.

An alternative to R^2 which is perhaps more useful when equations are being compared is the ratio: mean square due to regression/total mean square. This is the proportion of total *variance* accounted for by multiple regression. Whereas the addition of each new independent variable to an equation increases R^2 towards unity, the proportion of total *variance* accounted for can reach a maximum of less than unity and subsequently decline as further predictors are added; although R^2 continues to increase, the precision of estimation by the equation progressively declines as this optimum number of independent variables is exceeded.

3. The Execution of Multiple Regression Analysis

3.1 Some Problems with the Data

Before undertaking MRA it is important to examine the gross relationship between the dependent variable and each independent variable. This preliminary information is obtained from a series of scatter diagrams in which the dependent variable is plotted against each independent variable in turn. Each relationship should appear to be linear, or nearly so. It has already been explained how non-linear responses of a dependent variable can be accommodated in a multiple regression equation by including appropriate independent variables such as power terms, but this does not obviate the need to seek linearity at the outset since MRA will describe the response to each X-variable as the best-fitting straight line. BOX and TIDWELL (1962) discuss the transformation of independent variables; often employed are logarithms, square roots and reciprocals. BARTLETT (1947) and BOX and COX (1964) also discuss the use of transformations.

SCHRÖDTER (1965) overcame the problem of non-linear responses of pathogens to temperature by using a temperature growth function g which has a linear relationship to temperature, and is the polynomial,

$$g = \sin^2(a_1 t + a_2 t^2 + a_3 t^3) \tag{7}$$

such that the growth function is zero when temperature (t) is at the maximum and minimum values for the pathogen, and unity at the optimum temperature. With the relevant cardinal temperatures, the constants in Eq. (7) can be calculated for any phase of pathogen growth, e.g. spore germination, mycelial extension. (See also KRANZ, p. 9).

The scatter diagrams are used to check a basic assumption for MRA other than linearity, namely, that the variation in the dependent variable which is not explained by the X-variables (i.e. the error), occurs at random, independently of the value of the X-variables. Small departures from this homoscedasity are not important, but if the diagrams reveal large systematic changes in the variation of the dependent variable, the latter will require weighting (WILLIAMS, 1959) or transforming. The latter approach was why ROYLE and THOMAS (1972) expressed the dependent variable as *log* spore concentration.

Problems can arise over the nature of the dependent variable. When, for example, repeated measurements of disease severity or cumulative spore numbers are recorded, the data describe an epidemic *per se* and are expected to conform, more or less, to the S-shaped curves of disease progress. Whether the object of MRA is the formulation of a predictive equation for forecasting disease severity (BURLEIGH et al., 1972a), or the analysis of factors controlling rate of disease increase (ANALYTIS, 1973), it is necessary to linearize the disease progress data which constitute the dependent variable. Suitable transformations are considered by VAN DER PLANK (1963) and KRANZ (pp. 22 to 24), MOGK (p. 69), and JOWETT et al. (pp. 125) in other chapters of this book.

Other problems arise when successive observations of some feature of an epidemic are not independent, but constitute a time series in which the value of each observation is determined in part by its position in the series. If it is hoped to identify key factors in the environment it is advantageous to remove from the dependent variable those time-dependent components of its variation which are characteristic of time series, such as long-term trends, short-term periodicity (cycling or seasonality) and "stickiness". In econometric studies it is common to have dependent and independent variables forming time series and a useful expedient is to work with differences between consecutive observations (GOLDBERGER, 1964). Another approach is discussed elsewhere (p. 24).

Time series are often a feature of the dependent variable in epidemiology. Consider for example the concentration of inoculum recorded at 6-hour intervals. If observations are made over a long term, during which the epidemic generating the inoculum is developing, then fluctuations in concentration due to the effect of environmental factors will be superimposed upon the relatively smooth trend of disease progress. This trend can be eliminated before MRA is undertaken by using as the dependent variable not the original counts, but their deviations from running or block means, or alternatively, differences between consecutive counts in the series.

Periodicity, which will be a problem if sporulation or spore discharge is diurnal or nocturnal, can be tested for by a correlogram analysis which measures the correlation between pairs of observations in the series when the pairs are separated by various intervals. The effect of periodicity in a dependent variable can be removed by working with deviations from the mean of equivalent positions in the cycle, e.g. from the mean of each of the four daily 6-hour periods.

Finally, observations may be "sticky" due to correlation between observations in the time series. This is revealed by plotting each observation (Y_t) of the dependent variable against the preceding observation Y_{t-1}, and against Y_{t-2} etc. Suggestions of a relationship in these scatter diagrams can be verified by serial correlation coefficients. ROYLE and THOMAS (1972) avoided "stickiness" in a dependent variable by dividing a time series of daily values into 4-day units shown to be independent of oneanother.

An alternative approach to handling time series data is to employ independent variables which allow for time dependence in the dependent variable. An autoregressive multiple regression equation of the form,

$$\hat{Y}_t = b_0 + b_1 X_1 + b_2 X_2 + b_3 Y_{t-1} \tag{8}$$

allows the regression of Y on variables X_1 and X_2 to be measured independently of autoregression in the dependent variable, caused by correlation between consecutive observations Y_t and Y_{t-1} in the time series. Dummy variables can be employed to allow for linear time trends (DRAPER and SMITH, 1966). (Dummy variables can also be used to represent attributes such as cultivar, standard of management, etc.). A disadvantage of using independent variables to allow for the effect of time is that these predictors may be too efficient, and account for variation in the dependent variable at the expense of sensitivity in identifying and measuring the biological and meteorological factors which are being analysed. This does not matter if the only objective of MRA is prediction, and a high R^2 value is needed.

3.2 Assembling a Multiple Regression Equation

Deviations of predicted from observed values of the dependent variable should, if the regression model fits the data, be *random* error [e in Eq. (1)], without any systematic component, and after a regression equation has been calculated much can be learnt from graphs of these residuals plotted against each independent variable. Systematic variation of the residuals when plotted in this way shows that the model which has been proposed is not appropriate, and new analyses are undertaken with new or transformed independent variables to take account of the sources of variation disclosed in the residuals. For example, the introduction of variable X_3^2 into Eq. (6) could have followed a graphical observation of a non-linear relationship between the residuals obtained from a previous equation and variable X_3. DRAPER and SMITH (1966) give an excellent account of this aspect of testing which can reveal time trends, heteroscedasity and non-linear responses.

When a predictive equation is to be assembled it may be necessary to reduce many possible independent variables to the least number required for a satisfactory estimate of Y. If the preliminary number of candidate variables is not too large the regressions of Y on all combinations of the X-variables can be calculated to find the set which gives the smallest residual mean square. As the number (v) of candidate variables increases, the number of analyses needed ($2^v - 1$) to find the best sub-set increases rapidly; with seven there are 127 possibilities.

There are computer methods which expedite the search for the best set of predictors. In the forward selection method, preliminary simple regressions of Y on each candidate X-variable permits the selection of the X-variable which gives the highest regression sum of squares. The regression of Y on two independent variables is next calculated, each remaining variable being coupled in turn with the one first selected, and the pair is selected which gives the largest significant increase in regression sum of squares. The method progresses forward in this way to triplets, etc., so that variables are added to the equation in a descending order of importance. The backward elimination method operates in reverse, beginning with the multiple regression of Y on all the candidate independent variables. Then follows the elimination of variables in an ascending order of importance; at each stage the variable removed is the one whose absence leads to the least reduction in the regression sum of squares. The stepwise method (EFROYMSON, 1962) provides for both the inclusion and deletion of X-variables at each step. Furthermore, at each step all the selected variables are re-examined, as if each was the last to be selected.

The "best" regression equations assembled by these computer programs do not necessarily agree with one another, or with the best equation obtainable from the calculation of all possible combinations (HAMAKER, 1962). This is especially true if the independent variables are intercorrelated. In considering the choice between forward and backward methods, MOORE (1962) concludes that if the objective is to select very few predictors from a large number of X-variables the forward procedure will give an equation similar to the best obtainable from all combinations. If, however, the selection of say, five out of seven is needed, the backward method is more appropriate. ABT (1967) also advocates the backward method in certain cases and recommends that variables be examined by both methods. LARSON and BAN-CROFT (1963) discuss methods to be used when there is *a priori* knowledge of the order of importance of the independent variables.

4. The Interpretation of Relationships Exposed by Multiple Regression Analysis

The interpretation of multiple regression equations is limited by several considerations. First, and this is a point already noted, evidence of regression is not evidence of causation. Nevertheless, if a list of candidate independent variables is compiled in the light of some knowledge of the system being investigated, the relationships identified by MRA cannot be dismissed as meaningless.

Second, some key factors may not be included among the variables from which an equation is assembled. This type of omission is indicated when the accuracy of prediction by an equation varies according to the source of data with which it is fed. Alternatively, if several equations containing identical variables are assembled from data collected from various sources, the omission of important factors will be evident from the instability (inconsistency) of the partial regression coefficients. It should be noted, however, that if prediction is the only aim of MRA then the omission of key factors will not matter providing these are highly correlated with one or more of the predictors in an otherwise reliable equation.

Third, an equation may not predict accurately when the joint values of the independent variables lie outside the X-space of the values used in calculating the equation. To reduce this danger of extrapolating outside the experience of the original data, the latter should be wide-ranging and representative of the conditions for which the equation is expected to be used.

Finally, limitations are imposed by intercorrelations between the X-variables. At its simplest, false interpretation can occur when importance is assumed for an unimportant independent variable which is highly correlated with a missing key factor. The difficulties extend, however, to assigning relative importance to the X-variables in an equation. In laboratory and growth-chamber studies the control exercised by the experimental design and the experimenter allows the response to each treatment to be measured independently, so that the variables are not intercorrelated. The situation is different when features of an epidemic, like air-borne inoculum, infection periods and crop loss are measured in holistic field experiments in which multitudes of uncontrolled factors act and interact simultaneously. Although MRA is a useful method for probing the complex, the extensive intercorrelations in natural systems make the identification of key variables very difficult.

Intercorrelations between independent variables do not impede the assembly of predictive equations with high R^2 values because R^2 indicates the *combined* contribution of these variables to variation in the dependent variable. What is made difficult is an accurate estimation of partial regression coefficients; in an equation with a high R^2 it is possible to have low partial regression coefficients which are not significant. The reason is that if X_1 and X_2 are highly correlated and important variables, then when Y is regressed on X_1 in the presence of X_2 the net contribution of X_1 to the variation in Y will be low because X_2, a good predictor, itself accounts for most of the variation. The reverse applies when Y is regressed on X_2 in the presence of X_1. Therefore, although R^2 will be high, each partial regression coefficient may be non-significant due to this mutual interference between X_1 and X_2. The consequences of intercorrelation are often seen when consecutive equations assembled in a forward or backward selection procedure are compared; a variable which is very significant (or non-significant) at one stage suddenly becomes non-significant (or significant) when a new X-variable enters the equation. To interpret this behavior it is necessary to refer to a correlation matrix in order that the degree of association between variables is known.

Problems caused by intercorrelation can be reduced by selecting, with the aid of a correlation matrix, candidate X-variables which are not highly correlated. ANALYTIS (1973) adopted this pre-selection technique before he employed MRA to screen variables affecting apple scab epidemics.

It is possible to attribute degrees of importance to each of the independent variables assembled in a multiple regression equation, but for this it is important that there should be no intercorrelations (MOTT, 1966). The method of path coefficients (WRIGHT, 1954, 1960) requires the drawing of a path diagram of real or assumed causal relationships and was used by ANALYTIS (1973) to assign degrees of importance to three variables which had been identified by MRA as affecting the severity of apple scab on individual leaves. (See Section 5.3). The same author also used component vector analysis for a similar purpose.

5. The Applications of Multiple Regression Analysis in Epidemiology

We will now examine how, and to what effect, MRA is being used in epidemiology within the five schemes of analysis outlined in the Introduction.

When the object of analysis is solely to forecast the position an epidemic is expected to have reached at a future point in time, then the function of MRA is to select good predictors for this purpose, and these need not have a particular biological or physical rationale. The value of the method in this application lies in its ability to assemble predictive equations rather than in its capacity to analyze relationships between variables. Accordingly, there is no need to take account of time trends in the data, especially as the inclusion of such characteristics may contribute to the predictive accuracy of the equations. Indeed, some predictors may be deliberately chosen because their relationship with the dependent variable is time-dependent. The principal requirements are a high value of R^2 and reliability of the equation in future. Alternatively, if the object is not to forecast but to describe the quantitative relationships between time and successional observations of the dependent variable, then independent variables which are themselves measures of time, and therefore inevitably correlated with the dependent variable, are used.

When the object is to use MRA for a more analytical purpose, to explore and measure relationships between variables which describe the biological and physical aspects of the disease system, the independent variables must be selected rationally, in the light of knowledge or suspicions of causal relationships. Furthermore, and in contrast to the situations in the preceding paragraph, time-dependent relationships between the dependent variable and some independent variables can spoil the chances of success by accounting for too much of the variation in the dependent variable, thereby reducing the sensitivity with which other variables can be screened. It is therefore advantageous to eliminate correlations associated with time trends before MRA commences. (See 3.1.).

5.1 Progress of the Epidemic

In these examples the primary interest is a dependent variable which constitutes a time series, and which follows the path of disease progress.

As a measure of the progress of stem and leaf wheat rusts caused by *Puccinia graminis* f. sp. tritici and *P. recondita* f. sp. *tritici*, respectively, DIRKS and ROMIG (1970) in the U.S.A. undertook to forecast, separately for each species, cumulative numbers of uredospores at various intervals from 7 to 42 days in advance, according to the general plan of analysis shown in Fig. 26.

Their data, collected over 5 separate years on spring and winter wheat crops, were the number of spores trapped on slides which had been exposed daily at several sites during a period of each cereal-growing season. Data from 72 site-years represented a wide range of disease development. The dependent variable was expressed as the logarithm of the cumulative number of uredospores trapped from the day of the first catch each season. Eleven independent variables were examined of which five ($X_1 - X_5$) were designated "biological" and six ($X_6 - X_{11}$) "climatolog-

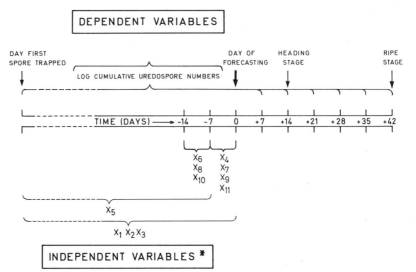

Fig. 26. Plan of analysis of cumulative spore numbers of *Puccinia graminis* and *P. recondita* as used by DIRKS and ROMIG (1970). Key to independent variables: X_1 Time (days). X_2 Cumulative number of *P. graminis* uredospores trapped/cm^2 of sticky slide (log-transformed). X_3 as X_2, but for *P. recondita*. X_4 Slope of the regression of the daily log cumulative number of uredospores trapped on time in days. X_5 as X_4, but over different time period. X_6 Rainfall function. X_7 as X_6, but over different time period. X_8 A spore germination function. X_9 as X_8, but over different time period. X_{10} A fungal growth function. X_{11} as X_{10}, but over different time period.
Note: X_4, X_5, X_8, X_9, X_{10}, and X_{11} calculated for the appropriate species

ical". Only two, however, (rainfall variables X_6 and X_7), were derived purely from meteorological measurements; $X_8 - X_{11}$ were temperature growth functions of spore germination and fungal growth derived from the polynomial equation of SCHRÖDTER (1965) (see 3.1). The predictive value of regression equations assembled separately for spring and winter wheats from (a) all variables, (b) "biological" variables only and (c) "climatological" variables only, was judged in terms of the total variation of the dependent variable explained by each equation. With all variables, significant R^2 values were obtained except for some forecasts of *P. graminis* spores in the winter wheat region. The equations of "biological" variables also gave significant values of R^2 for the *P. recondita* data, but were only significant for 14-day forecasts with *P. graminis*. "Climatological" variables used alone gave insignificant regressions, but the partial regression coefficients in equations in which all variables were incorporated suggested that although "climatological" variables were of little use in the prediction of *P. recondita*, the spore germination and fungal growth functions for the 7 days prior to the day of forecasting contributed to the prediction of *P. graminis*. As might be expected, the most consistently significant independent variables were those which best measured the severity of the epidemic at the time of forecasting, i.e. cumulative spore numbers up to this time (X_2 and X_3), for these took account of the time-dependent nature of the dependent variable.

According to previous studies (BURLEIGH et al., 1969), air-borne spore concentration is expected to relate to rust development but, since the trapping sites in the present study were not standardised in relation to sources of inoculum, Dirks and Romig did not regard their equations as suitable for forecasting disease progress. However, they considered their results showed that in the future, reasonable forecasts of cumulative spore numbers at heading could be made 14 days in advance with equations in which only two "biological" variables would be needed; a measure of disease severity on the day of forecasting and a measure of either the age or rate of the epidemic at that time. The addition of one "climatological" variable was expected to improve the prediction of *P. graminis* inoculum.

EVERSMEYER and BURLEIGH (1970), BURLEIGH et al. (1972a) and EVERSMEYER et al. (1973) set out to forecast the progress of wheat rusts during their development in plots of various spring and winter wheat cultivars at several localities in the Great Plains of the U.S.A. (Table 7). Weekly or twice-weekly counts of the number of uredia per culm were studied as the dependent variable, which therefore comprised accumulated disease severity at points along the progress curves. These data were transformed to logarithms in order to linearize disease progress with time (see 3.1). In the initial investigation (1970), leaf rust severity was forecast 8 days in advance at 24 winter wheat and 16 spring wheat sites in 1967 and 1968, using as predictors 7 biological and meteorological variables measured on or before the day of forecasting. At each site a standard susceptible cultivar was grown, together with a cultivar grown in the area and resistant to a proportion of the races within the prevalent population of the pathogen. In the light of their results, this system of analysis was subsequently modified for more detailed studies of both leaf (1972) and stem rust (1973) (Fig. 27) in which disease severity 7 (stem rust only), 14, 21, and 30 days ahead were dependent variables. Disease records from a larger number of sites and cultivars in 1969 and 1970, including representatives of all the recognised resistance genotypes grown in the Great Plains, were combined with the previous data for analysis. By collecting data from such wide ranging sources over the Great Plains where the climate is relatively uniform, the chance of obtaining predictive equations which would be reliable in future was greatly enhanced. An additional six independent variables were tested and, in the stem rust study, dummy variables described the cultivars and sites.

To evaluate up to 15 variables in all combinations would have required the calculation of nearly 33 000 equations, so the usual expedient of using a stepwise selection program was adopted. Six "best" equations emerged which would accurately estimate leaf rust on winter wheat, and there were four equations for spring wheat. The equations contained 2–5 variables, each of which contributed significantly to R^2. On spring wheat the equations accounted for 72% of the variation in leaf disease severity expected after 14 days and 67% after 30 days from the day of forecasting, while on winter wheat the corresponding figures were 64% and 57%. Encouraging results were also obtained for stem rust forecasts. Accurate forecasts with these equations were dependent upon the inclusion, as an independent variable, of an index of the quantity of inoculum present at the time the forecast was made; disease severity (DS) on the forecast date proved to be the best such index for both leaf and stem rust and indeed, the most important variable overall, alone accounting for 59–84% of the variation in leaf disease in 1967. When disease severity was omitted as an independent variable, one of the two variables describing cumulative spore numbers up to the day of prediction (CSN and WSN) became the most

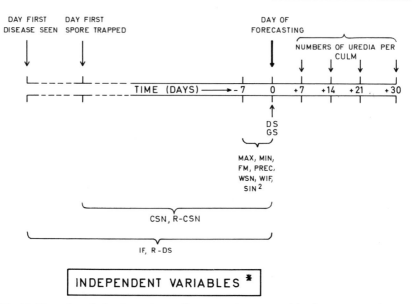

Fig. 27. Plan of analysis of cereal rust disease progress as used by BURLEIGH et al. (1972a) and EVERSMEYER et al. (1973). Key to independent variables: *DS* % rust severity (log-transformed). *CSN* Cumulative number of uredospores trapped/cm^2 of sticky slide (log-transformed). *WSN* Weekly spore number, as *CSN* but over different time period (log-transformed). *MIN* Minimum temperature, daily average. *MAX* Maximum temperature, daily average. *SIN^2* Sin^2 transformation of fungal growth rate. *GS* Growth stage of wheat, as integers on a 1–9 scale. *FM* Free moisture, as average h wetness, dew or rain. *PREC* Precipitation, number of days rainfall $\geqslant 0.25$ mm. $R-DS$ Logistic rate of increase in disease severity. $R-CSN$ Logistic rate of increase of cumulative spore numbers. *IF* Infection function; sum of daily evaluations of either 0 or 1 for each day, where 1 is considered favorable and 0 unfavorable for infection as judged by temperature, wetness and spore catch information

important variable, but there was a slight lowering of the R^2 value. CSN was the variable (X_2/X_3 in Fig. 26) which Dirks and Romig found to be the best in their equations. On winter wheat there were occasions when rust was absent on the day of forecasting; equations with alternative variables then satisfactorily forecasted leaf, but not stem rust up to 30 days in advance.

The accuracy of the leaf rust equations was demonstrated by forecasting disease severity on several cultivars of spring and winter wheat, and on one oat and one barley cultivar, with data not used in generating the equations. For leaf rust on winter wheat the average variation between observed and predicted values of the transformed variable was 1%, 3%, and 12% for 14-, 21-, and 30-day forecasts, respectively. There was no opportunity to examine the accuracy of the stem rust equations in a similar way but it was calculated from the standard error of the estimate in the regression analyses that it should be possible to forecast stem rust severities within 9% and 18% at 7 and 30 days, respectively.

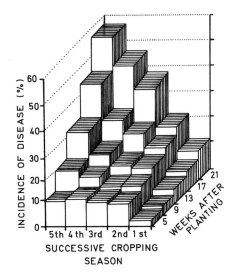

Fig. 28. Observed changes in the incidence of brown root rot primarily caused by *Pyrenochaeta lycopersici* on the roots of five successive tomato crops grown in the same untreated soil (LAST et al., 1969)

In their discussions of the results these workers point out that not all variables, or interactions between them, that affect rust development had yet been investigated. Even so, the variables are constructed largely from existing knowledge of causal relationships and it seems unlikely, therefore, that additional variables would improve substantially upon the accuracy of the predictions.

Having considered two examples in which predictive equations were improved by including some independent variables which were correlated with the dependent variable by virtue of time, we now turn to the work of LAST et al. (1969) with tomato brown root rot *(Pyrenochaeta lycopersici)*, in which *only* measures of time were used as independent variables. In an experiment in which tomato crops were grown in the same glasshouse for five successive years the incidence of brown root rot increased, both with time after planting within each season and with successive cropping seasons (Fig. 28). These workers sought the best multiple regression equation to describe the inevitable dependence of increasing disease on these two time factors. The percentage infected root area and three transformations of it, i.e. $\ln\left(\dfrac{1}{1-y}\right)$, which approximates to the multiple-infection transformation of GREGORY (1948), logit $\left(\ln\left(\dfrac{y}{1-y}\right)\right)$ and angular, were compared as dependent variables in an equation of the general form,

$$\hat{Y} = b_0 + b_1 X_1 + b_2 X_2 + b_{12} X_1 X_2 + b_{11} X_1^2 + b_{22} X_2^2 \tag{9}$$

where: X_1 = weeks after planting within seasons

X_2 = number of the year, when observations were made: 3 for 1963 (first year of crop), 4 for 1964, etc.

The regressions explained 72.6% (angular transformation), 71.3% (logit), 71.2% (untransformed %), and 67.7% (multiple infection) of the total variation in disease severity. With all expressions of the dependent variable there were significant first-order variables and with the multiple infection and logit transformations, significant quadratic variables which indicate curvature in the relationship. The graphs drawn from back-transformed angles and logits showed this non-linearity, which indicated that the build-up of brown root rot followed the compound interest pattern. These results were regarded as sufficiently promising to suggest the feasibility of predicting the time required for economically serious levels of disease to build up, enabling decisions to be made on the need for applying partial soil sterilants between crops.

The examples of disease progress studies considered so far have been directly concerned with specific diseases of economic importance, and with means to control them. KRANZ (1968a), however, was principally interested in the fundamental nature of the disease progress curve and sought to determine what general features of it could be recognised from a collective study of 59 fungal diseases of weed and crop hosts in tropical Guinea. Variation in the percentage of infected plants, recorded monthly on a 0–4 scale, was related to rainfall and temperature variables, and to integers describing growth stage, abundance of host plants and the progress in time by months. Interpretation of the correlation and partial regression coefficients with respect to the pooled data of the entire group of diseases showed that there was no universal effect of the meteorological variables on the diseases. Multiple regression equations from which the meteorological variables had been omitted revealed the importance of growth stage and host abundance as well as the expected relationship between disease rating and time. KRANZ (1968b, 1968c) proceeded to study the classification of epidemics and proposed twelve different models to summarise the observed progress curves (see p. 47).

5.2 The Rate of Disease Increase

When measurements of disease are made at relatively infrequent intervals during the course of an epidemic, the resulting progress curve appears as a smooth progression, as if some simple mathematical law were being obeyed. However, if records at short intervals are plotted, the irregularity of disease progress, due to the inconstant action of environmental factors on disease multiplication, becomes apparent. In this scheme of epidemic analysis, investigation is focused on the *true* rate of disease increase, so that the dependent variable is increments of disease in successive and relatively brief periods of time. If the climate is such that the weather causes wide fluctuations in disease multiplication, as in Northern Europe, then it may not be possible to estimate the true course of an epidemic unless the variables in the model endeavor to describe causally the response of the pathogen to its environment. There are two examples in which the rate of disease increase is investigated by MRA and in both, variables of this nature were included.

ANALYTIS (1973) used observations of apple scab *(Venturia inaequalis)* to appraise in great detail the mathematical/statistical treatment of epidemiological data from field investigations. During each of two seasons the degree of infection was

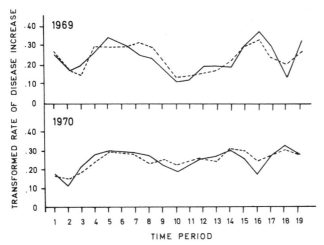

Fig. 29. Observed (solid line) and estimated (broken line) rates of disease increase of apple scab
(ANALYTIS, 1973)

measured by recording the number and diameter of scab lesions on individual leaves. The frequency distribution of the degree of infection was asymmetric. To meet the requirement of regression analysis the data were raised to the power 0.23. (For more details see p. 24).

MRA was used to investigate the dependence of the rate of disease increase, measured in successive 5-day periods, on fifteen biological and bio-meteorological variables most of which described responses of the pathogen to meteorological conditions. Each year only two variables were shown to be significant. The most important in both years was one describing the effect of temperature on spore germination during periods of leaf wetness, for which the hourly spore germination function was calculated from the $\sin^2$ equation of SCHRÖDTER (1965) and integrated over each wetness period. This variable was considered as a more precise substitute for the well-known Mills infection period. Additionally significant in 1969 was a variable which described the frequency of hourly temperatures in the range 18–20° C over a 2-day period, 10 days before each disease recording, while in 1970, an alternative variable consisting of an index of mycelial growth temperature response during the 10 days before each survey was significant; these two variables were highly intercorrelated. The two equations gave R^2 values of 0.713 for 1969 and 0.681 for 1970, and showed a good correspondence with the observed data (Fig. 29).

SCHRÖDTER and ULLRICH (1965) were concerned about a number of shortcomings in the various rules which had been advanced in the past to warn of attacks of potato blight *(Phytophthora infestans)* and proposed, as the basis of a new forecasting system, a multiple regression equation in which an attempt was made to synthesize, within a regression model, functionally-based expressions of the component events of disease multiplication.

The independent variables measured the effects of meteorological factors upon (a) spore germination and infection, (b) sporulation and (c) lesion expansion. The fourth variable expressed the effects of weather unfavorable to disease increase, i.e.

the effects of intervening dry periods. Each of these independent variables was a *complex* term constructed from fundamental information; for example, the sporulation term related sporulation to temperature during periods of at least 10 h with relative humidity $\geqslant 90\%$ or rainfall $\geqslant 0.1$ mm/h. According to Schrödter and Ullrich's model the total rate of disease increase in relatively short periods of the epidemic was partitioned between these four independent variables. Meteorological data were collected from various weather stations adjacent to plots of potatoes in which the disease was recorded at 2–3-day intervals. Variations in the length of the incubation period with temperature were incorporated into calculations of each variable.

Values of the independent variables were calculated using the meteorological data. The equation based upon the model gave fairly good estimates of the observed values of disease increase in the plots; approximately 56% of the variation in observations of disease increase was accounted for by allowing simple measurements of temperature and humidity/rainfall in the macroclimate to describe the various disease events in this way. Considering also that several assumptions regarding the nature of disease spread in the plots, growth of the host and host susceptibility had to be made initially, a large error was expected and this value of R^2 was considered acceptable. It was thought unlikely that the addition of other meteorological factors, e.g. wind or radiation, would improve these results. In a later paper, SCHRÖDTER and ULLRICH (1967) emphasized the causally-based origins of the variables in the prediction model and pointed out that, in having removed the inadequacies of previous warning rules, their method shows great promise for negative prognosis, i.e. predicting the duration of time in which the epidemic is not likely to develop in the early period of seasonal disease activity (p. 40).

5.3 Disease Severity

In this scheme of analysis we envisage the investigation of the level of disease severity reached at one time during a season. Commonly, for example, total disease present at the end of a season is analysed in terms of biological and physical factors occurring before or during the development of the disease. Such observations do not therefore form a time series and in this type of study there is no interest in forecasting disease progress *per se*. Multiple regression has been applied in this scheme to study simple and compound interest diseases (*sensu* VAN DER PLANK, 1963) in order to identify the key factors contributing to varying disease levels between seasons or geographical locations though, alternatively, the interest can be in prediction.

TALBOYS and WILSON (1970) wished to discriminate between rainfall and soil temperature as early-season factors associated with the eventual severity of hop wilt (*Verticillium albo-atrum*), and used data recorded for 15 years in plot experiments and over shorter periods in various hop gardens. The percentage of wilted plants of several cultivars (the dependent variable) was regressed on mean soil temperature (t), total rainfall (r), t^2, r^2, and the interaction term tr, these independent variables being expressed for various periods in the same growing season. In simple regressions with data from resistant cultivars, soil temperature and its square term were both significant, thus confirming the importance of this factor which had been suspected from previous evidence. Rainfall, r^2 and tr were not significant and a comparison of multiple regression equations from which each of the five variables was deleted in sequence indicated that mean soil temperature was the only variable accounting for a significant part of variation in wilt incidence. It was therefore concluded that low soil temperature in early summer is the main determinant of wilt incidence in cultivars with some degree of resistance. From these results it could have been concluded that rainfall has no influence. However, from their visual examination of some of the data, these authors recognised some contribution of high rainfall to the incidence of wilt. The failure of the analysis to confirm this may have been due to the small number of occasions when high rainfall was recorded.

The proportion of virus-infected plants within sugar-beet root crops was studied by WATSON and HEALY (1953) who used MRA to identify the biological factors thought to be of importance in field-to-field variation in disease. The incidence of beet yellows and mosaic diseases was recorded during 6 years in over 100 fields selected because they were either relatively close to or distant from sugar-beet seed crops. At the field sites counts were made throughout each season of winged aphids caught in sticky traps and of wingless forms on the plants. Transformations were applied to stabilize the variance of the disease data, used as the dependent variable, and to linearise the relationships between disease and the independent variables. MRA revealed that the number of winged peach-potato aphids *(Myzus persicae)* had the greatest influence on the spread of beet yellows and attributed some additional significance to the number of wingless forms. The analysis discounted winged and wingless forms of the bean aphid *(Aphis fabae)* as important vectors. Inclusion of the area of seed crops grown in the vicinity of the root crops as an additional independent variable significantly increased the variation explained by multiple regression, and it was therefore concluded that infection is increased in districts where seed crops are common. Proximity of seed crops did not influence the relationship between disease and aphid numbers because a variable describing the interaction between aphid numbers and area of seed crops did not have a significant partial regression coefficient.

A simple mathematical model of the spread of yellows was built from fundamental knowledge and was based upon the evidence from regression of the importance of winged aphids to the disease. When values of infection calculated by this model were regressed on observed infection, over 80% of the variance (not R^2) of observed disease was accounted for and was significantly improved by the addition of seed crop area, but not by wingless *M. persicae,* as an additional variable. The authors considered that no other factor of major importance to disease spread had been omitted.

Multiple regression failed to associate either species of aphid with the incidence of mosaic disease, despite the fact that winged forms of both species were considered equally to be vectors of the virus.

These results illustrate particularly well how multiple regression is an invaluable analytical tool when the investigation is necessarily a study of natural field events. It is difficult to conceive how else the relationship between disease and vectors migrating from their winter hosts on to and among a crop might be evaluated.

ANALYTIS (1973) set out to determine to what extent observations of disease on separate leaves (see 5.2) recorded on the last assessment date each year were affected by host and disease/host factors, which he called "phenometric" variables. It was initially assumed that disease severity depended entirely on phenometric variables though this was recognised to be an oversimplification.

The 16 candidate independent variables were examined with a correlation matrix and pre-selected, reducing their number to 12. This reduced the intercorrelations which impede the screening of variables. The data were then subjected to a stepdown selection method of MRA which eliminated all but three independent variables with significant partial regression coefficients, and which largely accounted for the variation in disease severity on individual leaves in both years. These variables were leaf age (the order of unfolding), the date on which the disease was first recorded on a leaf, and the type of scab spots (e.g. necrotic). R^2 values of 0.449 and 0.509 were obtained for each year, respectively, which suggests that other variables, possibly meteorological ones, were missing. ANALYTIS then demonstrated the method of path coefficients (WRIGHT, 1954, 1960) as a means of assigning degrees of relative importance to the three significant phenometric variables, on the assumption that they are causally related to disease severity. This aspect of interpretation is referred to in Section 4 above.

The previous examples are concerned entirely with screening rationally-chosen variables measured during disease development and which are assumed to influence the level of disease encountered at the end of the growing season. In contrast, forecasting the annual incidence of virus yellows in sugar-beet crops was the aim of WATSON (1966) who based her analysis on the principle that flights of the aphid vectors in summer are influenced by meteorological conditions during the previous winter and early spring. Freezing is probably important in determining aphid survival in winter and HURST (1965) had previously concluded that the mean daily air temperature in February had a major effect which could be modified by the temperature in March and April. Watson utilized this information to relate, using MRA, the annual incidence of beet yellows infection at the end of August to two variables: the number of days in January-March when the temperature fell below 0° C, and the temperatures in April expressed as the deviation from a long-term mean. Variables were transformed to linearize relationships and to stabilize variance. Multiple regression equations compiled for two periods, the years 1940–49 and 1950 onwards, and containing both independent variables, gave very good agreement between observed and predicted values for 1950 onwards (Fig. 30 A), suggesting the possibility of a forecasting system. With data before 1950 however, different partial regression coefficients were obtained and the fit of the regression was not so good (Fig. 30 B). The equations could not be tested with new data since this, of course, did not exist. Discussing these results the author makes the valid and general point that even though biologically-meaningful variables were used to describe variations in disease severity, the regression equations may not be appropriate to all years or all situations. In this analysis, temperature in April was found to be more important as a predictor before than after 1950, probably because before 1950, aphids that survived low temperatures during moderate winters acquired more virus from infected seed crops during the early summer than they did after 1950; before 1950, seed crops were the main source of viruses for the root crop, afterwards they

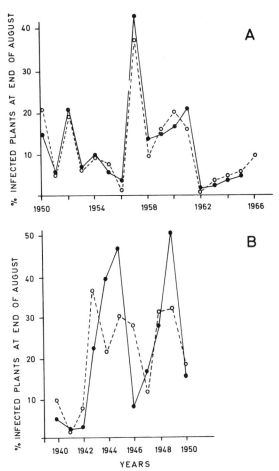

Fig. 30 A and B. Observed values for per cent plants with beet yellows (solid circles) compared with predicted values (open circles), (A) for years 1950–1965; (B) for years 1940–1949 (WATSON, 1966)

became much less important. Also, April temperatures before 1950 were generally above average and probably allowed aphids to multiply early and spread virus more effectively. Therefore during the period covered by this study, both climate and management changed. This illustrates a general warning that predictive equations are likely to become less accurate as time from the date of their compilation passes, and it may be good practice to assemble new equations each year using the experience of only the *most recent* years. An increase in accuracy of prediction would probably compensate for the loss of data with which to calculate equations.

5.4 Events in the Disease Cycle

It is common practice to study events like sporulation, infection and spore dispersal by conducting experiments in the controlled conditions of incubators, growth-rooms, wind tunnels etc., where responses to one or two factors nominated as treatments can be measured independently of the effects of other factors. The conditions of such experimentation oversimplifies the real field situation in which these cyclic activities of the pathogen are inevitably influenced by many interacting factors. Multiple regression analysis provides a facility for screening variables which are believed to affect these events in the natural system, and we shall now examine several examples of this scheme of application. First, however, we shall consider an application of MRA to controlled factors in the analysis of pathogen activities by MASSIE (1973), in his investigation of southern corn leaf blight with race *T* of *Helminthosporium maydis* on a susceptible male-sterile corn hybrid. MASSIE and NELSON (1973) outlined the nature of this study in which regression models were developed to relate sporulation, spore take-off, spore germination and infection to key factors determining each event. Only the analysis of sporulation has so far been published in some detail (MASSIE et al., 1973) and this is now to be discussed.

The object was to use multiple regression techniques to quantify the response of sporulation to environmental regimes. This study was unusual in the fitting of multiple regression equations to data obtained in *controlled experiments* in glass-house and growth-room (NELSON and TUNG, 1973) in which the *fundamental* relationship of sporulation (Y) to length of dew period (X_1) and dew temperature (X_2) were measured (Fig. 31 A). Sporulation was recorded as the number of spores/ mm^2 of lesion on seedling plants. Dew periods in the range 12–24 h were established in combination with several temperatures in the range 12–30° C. Because of problems in fitting a single model to the data, separate analyses were undertaken for the response of sporulation to (a) a 24 h dew period at all temperatures, (b) a 30° C dew temperature at all dew periods except 24 h, (c) all other combinations of dew period and temperature. A preliminary model utilizing both independent variables and their interactive term $X_1 X_2$ was inadequate, so it was expanded to include further expressions of these variables. Transformation of the dependent variable to $\sqrt[4]{Y}$ finally provided equations which predicted sporulation in each of the three segments of analysis with R^2 values in the range 0.936–0.999. High values of R^2 are favored by the nature of the transformed dependent variable. The three equations were used to estimate sporulation in the same experiments which provided the data for the calculation of the equations; the fit was good (Fig. 31 B).

Prediction of sporulation on infected leaves removed from field plants was attempted. The lesions were washed free of spores, placed in dew chambers and subjected to six combinations of dew period and dew temperature. Reasonably accurate agreement was obtained between observed and predicted levels of sporulation (Fig. 32). These workers made no attempt to predict sporulation in the field under natural conditions and complete confidence in the equations must depend on this since there may be effects on sporulation of interactions between other components of the weather and the determinants used in these equations. For instance, light was shown by NELSON and TUNG (1973) to influence sporulation of *H. maydis* markedly. The formulae may not be applicable to all *H. maydis* isolates on all corn selections. Even so, the authors point out that their method demonstrates the quantification of one event in the disease cycle in a manner that may be employed in building comprehensive models. A consideration of this study in the context of modeling is discussed in Section 6.

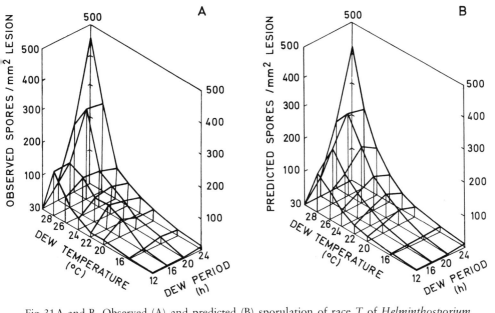

Fig. 31 A and B. Observed (A) and predicted (B) sporulation of race *T* of *Helminthosporium maydis* on Texas male-sterile corn, subjected to various combinations of dew period and temperature during the dew period (MASSIE et al., 1973)

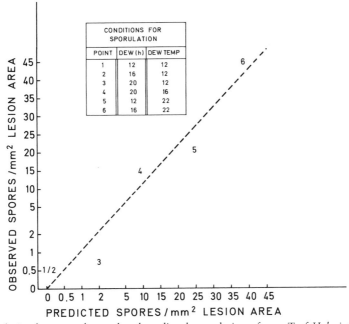

Fig. 32. Relation between observed and predicted sporulation of race *T* of *Helminthosporium maydis* on mature Texas male-sterile corn, subjected to various combinations of dew period and temperature during the dew period (MASSIE et al., 1973)

The polycyclic events of the disease cycle can be difficult to measure in the field. It is convenient to observe these events by using traps, either artificial (e.g. suction traps, sticky cylinders) or living plants, which confine measurements of the events to brief, discrete periods of time. Although serial observations of the dependent variable may still constitute a time series, as with the data of DIRKS and ROMIG (1970) (see 5.1), corrections for this can be made if necessary (see 3.1).

Artificial traps confine investigations to inoculum concentration and deposition. Multiple regression has been employed to analyze trap data of aerial spore concentrations of tobacco powdery mildew *(Erysiphe cichoracearum)* by COLE (1966), apple powdery mildew *(Podosphaera leucotricha)* by BUTT (1968, 1969, 1972a), and hop downy mildew *(Pseudoperonospora humuli)* by ROYLE and THOMAS (1972).

Cole mainly used simple regressions to relate hourly and daily concentrations of conidial flights in tobacco plantations to a selection of meteorological variables. Only occasions when conidial concentrations exceeded an unspecified level were included in the analysis. In some years variables describing air temperature and vapor pressure deficit were significantly correlated with daily total spore concentrations; MRA was used to screen these intercorrelated variables and the result emphasised the relative importance of temperature. Over four years no variable was consistently associated with spore concentration but treatment of the data to remove, for example, time trends in the dependent variable, may yield more conclusive results.

Butt's objective was to determine the factors responsible for fluctuations of airborne concentrations of apple powdery mildew conidia on rain-free summer days. He analysed the dependence of spore concentration on five meteorological variables: wind, rain, vapor pressure deficit, temperature and leaf wetness. Periodicity, seasonal trends and "stickiness" between consecutive counts were demonstrated in the dependent variable and eliminated before proceeding with the regression analyses. The results, not yet published in detail, exposed vapor pressure deficit from midnight to 0600 h on the night preceding spore release as the most important variable, with day temperature and total rain in the 6-day period before spore dispersal also significant. The importance of humidity at night is consistent with the observation that spores initiated at night form an important part of the crop of spores released during the following daytime.

The main purposes of the investigation by Royle and Thomas were to produce a predictive equation to enable the forecasting of downy mildew spore concentrations in hop gardens using simply-obtained meteorological measurements, and to screen variables expected to be causatively associated with variation in daily spore flights. To achieve the latter objective it was necessary to remove time series effects from the data. The dependent variable was the logarithm of the maximum hourly spore concentration (the "release period") in consecutive 4-day periods in the summers of 1967 and 1968. The independent variables were six meteorological factors, known or thought to affect sporulation and spore release, expressed in 6-hour periods during the 3 days preceding each "release period". The weather factors were relative humidity $(h \geq 90\%)$, temperature (mean), vapor pressure deficit (mean), leaf wetness (h), rainfall $(mm$ and $h)$ and daily sunshine duration. Simple correlations and multiple regression analyses identified several significant variables but no variable assumed to be causative was consistently associated with spore release. One equation, based on rainfall duration, temperature and vapor pressure deficit in various periods prior to the "release period" gave the highest R^2 values (0.65, 0.53 and 0.55 for 1967, 1968, and 1967 + 1968 data respectively) and was then examined for prediction (Table 4). This equation gave a reasonable agreement between observed and predicted values when each year's data were estimated using data of the other year. But when new data collected in 1969 and 1970 were used with the same equation some seriously inaccurate estimates of spore concentration were obtained. Two reasons were thought to be responsible for this failure. First, extrapolation probably occurred, so that the equation estimated erroneously new data which lay outside the range of the independent variables used in calculating the equation. Second, inconsistent partial regression coefficients suggested that some variables were missing from the equation. These were likely to be biological ones which, although less convenient as predictors, probably play a key role in spore production.

In the past, the use of living potted plants as traps to monitor and measure various events of the disease cycle has not enjoyed wide appeal. This is partly because of the difficulties in producing large numbers of healthy plants in a condition which simulates that of naturally-grown ones, and partly in accommodating the plants free from contamination before and after exposure to natural infection. JENKYN et al. (1973) have designed and tested an apparatus for growing cereal plants in isolation for this type of study. The advantages of living plants for monitoring events in the disease cycle are several. In particular, they enable variations in spore deposition, infection, incubation and sporulation to be interpreted in terms of environmental factors operating in prescribed time periods. Living plants have been used to detect infection periods (e.g. PREECE, 1964; BUTT, 1969, 1970, 1972a; TU and HENDRIX, 1970; LAPWOOD, 1971) and MRA has been applied to data of this kind by SNOW et al. (1968) and ROYLE (1973). In these studies, measurements of disease on the plants constituted the dependent variable, but since the disease resulted from the exposure of the plants at an earlier date to natural inoculum and weather, the conditions affecting infection severity were the real subject of investigation.

SNOW et al. wished to determine the relationship between infection of slash pine (*Pinus elliottii* var. *elliottii*) by fusiform rust (*Cronartium fusiforme*) and weather and inoculum. They monitored infections due to basidiospores by exposing batches of seedling pines daily for a period of 22–24 h, in a stand of oak trees bearing the telial stage of the fungus. After exposure, plants were first incubated in standard conditions for 24 h and then planted in a nursery where further infection was prevented by regular applications of fungicide. The percentage of diseased plants ranged from 0–69% in 30 exposures in 1965 and 0–60% in 21 exposures in 1966. Batch values less than 3% were attributed to background contamination during incubation and excluded from the analyses. The percentage of diseased seedlings, the dependent variable, was regressed on twelve independent variables which described the weather before and during exposure, the total spore catch and the time spores were trapped during exposure.

The authors give very few numerical details of the results of the regression analyses, probably because infection severity was clearly associated with certain combinations of environmental conditions. However, simple linear regressions identified the number of hours in which relative humidity was greater than 97% during seedling exposure as a consistently significant variable in each year. Two inoculum variables were also significant, but in 1965 only. A stepwise program of multiple regression of the 1965 data identified the total number of basidiospores trapped during the exposure period as the most important variable; additional variables failed to contribute further to R^2. Some transformations of the data might have been rewarding in achieving more results. For instance, the measure of the dependent variable failed to allow for the effect of spores coming into contact with previously infected plants and the application of the multiple-infection transformation (GREGORY, 1948) to the percentage data would probably have been helpful.

In experiments over three growing seasons, potted hop plants were used by ROYLE (1973) to monitor natural infections of downy mildew. This study has produced some useful, rationally-based predictive equations and at the same time has nicely illustrated some of the limitations in explaining natural disease using regression models. Successive daily batches of plants were exposed for 48-h periods in an unsprayed hop garden, and then incubated free from further infection and under standard conditions. Variations in the severity of leaf disease were then explained by MRA in terms of conditions experienced during the exposure period. The identification of good predictors was the main objective, but the screening of variables with known causal relationships to infection (ROYLE, 1970) was also of interest. Of several dependent variables examined, the % leaves infected, transformed by the logarithm of the multiple-infection transformation (GREGORY, 1948) was finally chosen. Of one biological (air-borne spore concentration) and eight meteorological variables tested, five intercorrelated variables describing wet conditions were each correlated significantly with infection severity. MRA identified the duration of rain-wetness as the most important independent variable, thereby providing evidence to support previous suspicions that surface wetness caused by dew failed to provide conditions for severe infection. It is interesting to note that although the air-borne spore variable was not itself correlated with infection, it contributed significantly to multiple regression equations containing one or more of the wetness variables. In this disease infection is, of course, limited to periods when there is free water on the foliage, and these conditions do not always coincide with the availability of inoculum. Equations containing all the independent variables accounted for 74–90% of the variation in infection, depending upon the year. Equations which included rain-wetness duration, rainfall quantity and air-borne spores as significant variables (Table 13) gave the best prediction of each year's infection when calculated from the combined data of the other two years (Fig. 33).

The additive nature of this equation means that even though leaves may be dry when spores are caught, or spores may be absent when wetness is recorded, a value for infection is predicted. Therefore, though the multiple regression analysis identified biologically meaningful variables, the best equation it produced was intrinsically illogical because of the additive nature of the model, and as may be seen from Fig. 33, overestimates were therefore occasionally obtained, e.g. periods 27 and 28 in 1971. In general, however, the equation predicted infection sufficiently accurately for practical purposes. As we have seen in other examples, although the structure of a multiple regression model is additive, this does not preclude the

Table 13. Details of the best regression equations in the analysis of infection in hop downy mildew *(Pseudoperonospora humuli)*(ROYLE, 1973)

		Source of data			
		All three years	1969 + 1970	1969 + 1971	1970 + 1971
Partial regression coefficients:	Rain-wetness duration (h)	0.023^b	0.023^b	0.025^b	0.016^a
	Rainfall amount (mm)	0.066^b	0.061^b	0.061^b	0.100^b
	Air-borne spores (no./m³ air)	0.002^b	0.004^b	0.002^a	0.002^b
Intercept:		0.037	−0.063	0.081	0.070
R^2:		0.702	0.772	0.674	0.672

Significantly different from 0: [a] at $\leq 5\%$ level, [b] at $\leq 1\%$ level.

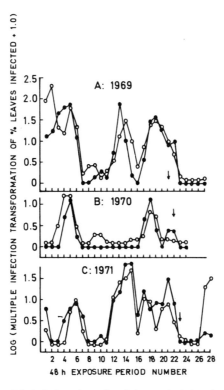

Fig. 33 A–C. Observed (solid circles) and predicted (open circles) values for infection by hop downy mildew: (A) 1969 data predicted from an equation utilizing rain-wetness duration, rainfall amount and air-borne spore concentration, based on 1970 + 1971 data; (B) 1970 data predicted from the same variables based on 1969 + 1971 data; (C) 1971 data predicted from the same variables based on 1969 + 1970 data. The arrows indicate the exposure period beginning 1. June in each year (ROYLE, 1973)

expression of products and interactions between variables. Thus the interaction between rain-wetness duration and air-borne spores could have been allowed for by including their product as an independent variable. The effect of this on the accuracy of prediction is at present being explored.

Some overestimates of infection by the regression equation, e.g. periods 1 and 2 in 1969, were because rainfall in 1969 exceeded the range encountered in 1970 and 1971 which had been used in the calculation of the equation, but in general, extrapolation problems of this kind were not serious. An equation derived from data taken from all the years is expected to cope with the effect of occasional heavy rain. Underestimates of severe levels of infection, e.g. period 13 in 1969 and periods 14, 15, and 21 in 1971, occurred because regression equations failed to accommodate sequences of events within the 2-day exposure periods. In particular, the sequence of large spore release during the daily peak release period of 09–1300 h followed soon afterwards by prolonged rain-wetness was especially favorable for heavy infection, but this situation was not described by any of the variables used in the study. There is no reason why MRA should not embrace variables describing the order of events, though no examples of this are known.

This example of the use of MRA is considered in detail by WAGGONER (p. 138) in this volume to illustrate the limitations of a simple model, and he compares the method with simulation.

On susceptible varieties of hop, improved control of downy mildew will result if infection which will give rise to disease above a threshold level, estimated to be about 0.5 on the scale in Fig. 33, can be predicted. On this basis of evaluation the best equations (Table 13), and others using only two simply-measured meteorological variables, predicted correctly in over 90% of the exposure periods. Although a few constraints on use of the equations may be necessary for their practical application, this example of the use of MRA illustrates how the method can be used with success for purposes of control. First attempts to use multiple regression equations to predict infection in commercial hop gardens have been promising (ROYLE and LIYANAGE, 1973).

Blister blight of tea *(Exobasidium vexans)* proved to be a convenient disease for epidemiological field studies in Sri Lanka. One of the advantages is that the crop is harvested by frequently hand-plucking young shoots (two or three leaves and a bud) on which the disease can be conveniently assessed to provide an accurate measure of disease attributable to infection within relatively short periods of time. In a sense, the harvested shoot tips are used as living traps. Studies of the prediction of sporulation (KERR and SHANMUGANATHAN, 1966) are closely associated with the prediction of disease severity (KERR and RODRIGO, 1967 a), and therefore are considered together in this section.

Two multiple regression equations were assembled by KERR and RODRIGO (1967 a) to explain variation in the number of blisters/100 shoots in terms of daily spore concentration and daily duration of either surface wetness or sunshine during an "infection period" 15–25 days prior to each measurement of disease. These variables contributed significantly to variation in the dependent variable, though spore concentration was the most important. There was no significant difference in the predictive accuracy of the two equations, though both were considered unsatisfactory because of very high intercept values. Further equations used sunshine rather than wetness since most tea estates in Sri Lanka possessed sunshine but not wetness recorders. By expressing spore numbers (X_1) and sunshine (X_2) as the interaction term X_1X_2, and using this in place of X_2, the intercept was reduced to a value not significantly different from zero and therefore deleted from the equation. Both variables were significant. With this equation, estimated disease incidence was compared with observed values for one year's data and the correspondence was extremely good.

Spore traps are not common on tea plantations, but spore numbers could be estimated using regression equations developed previously by KERR and SHANMU-GANATHAN (1966), which related the number of spores/blister to disease incidence (number of blisters/100 shoots) and mean daily sunshine (Table 4). All variables were transformed to linearise relationships and separate equations were calculated for two periods, April to December excluding August, and August only.

Now the number of spores in a unit volume of air was found to equal the number of spores/blister multiplied by the number of blisters/unit area of leaf. Furthermore, since the number of blisters/unit area was proportional to the number of blisters/100 shoots multiplied by the daily yield of plucked shoots, then the mean number of spores/m³ air could be determined. When the accuracy of the equations for predicting air-borne spore concentration was tested on three years' data the agreement was sufficiently satisfactory to allow the equations to be used for estimating the number of spores/m³ air (X_1) needed for the equation of KERR and RODRIGO (1967a).

In later work (KERR and RODRIGO, 1967b) the calculations necessary to use the multiple regression equations for disease prediction were simplified after further application of MRA to the data (Table 6). Only two variables, percentage infection and sunshine duration, were required to forecast accurately disease incidence 2–3 weeks in advance. A simple calculator was produced so that tea planters could easily use the method and save applications of fungicide.

5.5 Crop Loss

The method of multiple regression has been used in several studies to explore and measure relationships between disease and crop loss. The inclusion of examples of this type in a chapter which deals with epidemiology is justified because the ultimate criterion of the importance of most epidemic diseases is their effect on the market value of crops, and also because measurements of disease progress have proved valuable for estimating crop losses.

SALLANS (1948) applied MRA to an examination of the effect of common root rot (*Helminthosporium sativum* and *Fusarium* spp.) on wheat production in Saskatchewan, Canada. He analyzed the regression of annual wheat yields (bushels/acre) in nine districts over ten years on: rainfall (inches) in the summer of each crop year (X_1), rainfall in the preceding autumn and spring (X_2), average daily mean temperature (°F) in the summer of each crop year (X_3), damage (%) due to insects (X_4) and the rating of common root rot (X_5). The annual disease rating in each district was obtained from a sample of 10–20 sites; the wheat yields were official crop statistics.

The addition of variable X_5 to the other four significantly increased the regression sum of squares and provided the relationship,

$$\hat{Y} = 39.91 + 1.61X_1 + 1.12X_2 - 0.56X_3 - 0.15X_4 - 0.58X_5 \qquad (10)$$

in which all the partial regression coefficients were significant, and with an R^2 of 0.78. Sallans concluded that the data supported the view that the disease was responsible for serious crop losses, but the net effect of the disease, as measured by the appropriate partial regression coefficient, was surprisingly large. This was explained in part by a large standard error, and in part by the probable omission of other key factors such as soil fertility.

In contrast to this analysis of crop statistics and survey data, WATSON et al. (1946) investigated the effect of beet yellows virus on the production of sugar-beet in experimental plots of four trials in which they planned to compare nominal infection rates (% infected plants) by applying infectious aphids to nominated proportions of the plant populations. The effect on yield of the time of infection was also to be measured by applying the aphids on successive dates. It was intended to maintain the infection rates at the nominal levels by the application of insecticide, but this failed to prevent the natural spread of virus into and within the plots, and plot yield differences at harvest had to be interpreted in terms of the progress of the epidemics which had been initiated.

The yield of sugar per plant (the only measure of productivity to be considered here) was assumed to regress on the number of plants showing symptoms for the first time on each observation date following the application of aphids. The partial regression coefficients therefore estimated the effect upon yield of symptoms first recorded on successive dates. The proportion of the variance (not R^2) of the observed yields accounted for by these multiple regression analyses in the four trials was in the range 53–94%, being lowest in years when natural infections were severe and early. When the partial regression coefficients were used to adjust the sugar yields to those expected at the intended nominal infection rates, the adjusted yields were found to be linearly related to the proportion of infected plants, indicating that there had been no compensatory yield increase of the healthy plants. Of considerable additional importance was the linear relationship between the observation dates (of first symptoms) and their respective partial regression coefficients, for this indicated that the loss of yield per plant was directly proportional to the total infected-plant-weeks prior to harvest, and revealed the possibility of estimating crop losses.

The next two studies differ from the foregoing in that estimation of crop loss was the specific objective of the work, rather than a by-product. In both investigations, estimates of crop loss were determined by building a regression model in which partial regression coefficients integrate the effect on yield of disease present at successive stages of crop development. For example, BURLEIGH et al. (1972b) used data from 55 cultivar x location x year combinations to assemble regression equations for the prediction of grain weight losses caused by leaf rust (*Puccinia recondita* f. sp. *tritici*) on wheat. Crop loss was measured as the percentage reduction of unsprayed plots below the yield of their fungicide-treated neighbors. Variables as predictors were disease severity (% rust infection) on the flag leaf (*F*) or per tiller (*T*), recorded at the boot (X_1), heading (X_2), early berry (X_3) and early dough (X_4) stages of plant development. A stepwise MRA program produced several equations in which each of these biological variables was significant, and gave a maximum R^2 value of 0.79. A typical equation was,

$$\hat{Y} = 5.38 + 5.53 X_{1(T)} - 0.33 X_{3(F)} + 0.50 X_{4(F)} . \tag{11}$$

The fit of this equation was fairly accurate at moderate and severe levels of crop loss but the equation overestimated low levels, suggesting that the relationship between disease and loss is not linear over the range of disease severity. It would be interesting to know the effect of including meteorological variables as predictors.

The amount of disease present at the heading stage did not appear to be detrimental to the yield of grain because in no analysis was the partial regression coefficient for this stage significant. Also of interest was the finding that partial regression coefficients for the early berry stage (X_3) were consistently negative, as in the equation above, indicating that either the net effect of disease at this stage is to increase grain weight, or that another factor or factors, positively correlated with this independent variable, can be detrimental to the yield of grain. Could such a factor be rainfall (BURLEIGH et al., 1972a)? It is noteworthy that the equations satisfactorily estimated crop losses when predicted severities of leaf rust (see 5.1) were used instead of observed severities (Table 8).

Of considerable epidemiological interest is the work of JAMES et al. (1972) on the effect of *Phytophthora infestans* on yield of potato tubers in Canada (Table 8). Foliage disease data, recorded on the plots of eleven fungicide trials, provided 96 diverse disease progress curves. The crop loss associated with each progress curve was calculated as the percentage reduction of tuber weight below the yield of the fungicide treatment which best controlled late blight in the same trial. Explanations of the variation in crop loss were attempted using the critical stage theory, the threshold theory and the area under the progress curve, but these methods were not as satisfactory as a model of the regression of crop loss on variables derived from increments of blight in nine consecutive weekly time periods, ending 30 September.

Some interesting subjective criteria were used in selecting the final equations. For example, partial regression coefficients with a negative sign were omitted because, it was argued, such variables have no logical place in a model which estimates crop loss. This contrasts with the negative coefficient discussed above in the cereal rust study. Also, in no single time period was the increment of disease permitted to have an excessively large net effect on the estimation of crop loss.

Two equations were selected, one for early and one for late epidemics. For 92% of the epidemics examined these equations estimated the crop loss to within 5% (in absolute terms) of the observed percentage loss. This illustrates the accuracy which can be achieved in forecasting crop losses when a suitable model integrates the successive effects on yield of a disease as it progresses in time. In this model there was no linear relationship between the value of the partial regression coefficients and time, as occurred with the results of WATSON et al. (1946).

6. Conclusions: The Place of Multiple Regression in Current Approaches to Epidemic Analysis

A multiple regression model explains responses in one variable (the dependent) as the sum of linear functions of other (the independent) variables, with little regard to the manner in which the independent variables exercise their control. A regression model is unlikely to describe pathways of causation in biological systems because the determining variables are assumed to act additively, and each is related *directly* to the responding (dependent) variable, not indirectly *via* the true paths of action, reaction and interaction. The description of real relationships is the target of functional models, an example of which is discussed by WAGGONER (p. 142) in this book. Notwithstanding the elementary form of regression, all models are simplified statements, and the degree of simplicity inherent in regression is acceptable if the model satisfies the objectives of the researcher.

In the hypothetical example used in (2), the number of lesions was assumed to be dependent upon spore dose (X_1), humidity (X_2) and wind speed (X_3). The regression equation measured the *net* effect of each of these variables on the variation in lesion numbers, and the probability of the respective relationships being significant could have been measured by statistical tests. The model did not indicate the intrinsic role of each variable in its effect on lesion numbers. Consider spore dose. In the interval between the spore cloud and the appearance of symptoms the pathogen had to be intercepted, and then survive, germinate, penetrate and complete many other stages of the disease cycle before terminating as visible lesions. Irrespective of these intermediate stages a relationship was exposed between spore dose and lesion numbers. Similarly for humidity and wind speed, their *functional* relationships with lesion production is not considered in the model, only their overall relationships with the end product, the lesions. In other words, the regression model describes at only one level of explanation, that of the end product, irrespective of whether this is lesions, inoculum concentration, rate of disease increase, crop loss or any other dependent variable.

Although functional relationships cannot be described by a regression equation, MASSIE (1973) has successfully used regression models in sub-routines of a simulator. Regression equations were calculated for key factors operating at various levels (i.e. stages) of the disease cycle; this study with respect to sporulation has been discussed in Section 5.4. When these sub-models were assembled into a computer program the ultimate model satisfactorily simulated disease progress. Massie notes that the sensitivity of the simulator to small changes in the independent variables is due to the method of quantification given by regression at each level.

The logic of quantifying responses at each level of a system is also evident in the model developed by SCHRÖDTER and ULLRICH (1965) and discussed in Section 5.2, but in contrast to MASSIE they used one equation only, in which complex independent variables related disease increase to each of several levels in the disease cycle.

Regression equations are empirical by nature, being the products of experiment and observation, and are based upon inductive reasoning from particular observed responses (to controlled or uncontrolled variables) to the general, and are therefore statements of what has been experienced. This is an inherent weakness of MRA because the models make no provision for the effects of unexpected factors such as changes in the weather pattern, pathogen population or system of crop management. WATT (1961) points out that a balance between deductive and inductive reasoning is a desirable approach to the synthesis of functional models which he names the mixed deductive-inductive type. The limitations of regression do not necessarily exclude deductive reasoning from *a priori* knowledge in the assembly of individual equations or in their use, and the models of Massie and Schrödter and

Ullrich are types in which regression plays a major part in the structuring of a functional model.

OORT (see BUTT, 1972b), described epidemiology as a branch of ecology concerned with the ecosystem in which host and pathogen co-exist, and in this chapter we have been mainly considering natural responses in this ecosystem. The value of partial regression coefficients is that they quantitatively evaluate variables and provide insight into factors which are important in causing responses. MRA plays an important role in the study of natural systems in animal ecology (WATT, 1966) as a bridge between field observations and the synthesis of models. Epidemiologists now recognise the value of studying the dynamics of disease within the realm of the ecosystem and KRANZ (1972) has considered the place of regression analysis in holistic field experiments (Fig. 4). We believe that MRA will have an increasingly important role in epidemiology, as a simple analytical tool for probing the complexities of the natural system, and as a springboard for further advances. DRAPER and SMITH (1966) state that "the multiple regression technique is a powerful tool ... but it is easily misused and misunderstood". We have attempted to explain the nature of multiple regression and the relevance of the technique to present-day epidemiology.

References

ABT, K.: On the identification of the significant independent variables in linear models. Metrika 12, 1–15 (1967).

ANALYTIS, S.: Methodik der Analyse von Epidemien dargestellt am Apfelschorf [*Venturia inaequalis* (Cooke) Aderh.]. Acta Phytomedica 1, 1–76 (1973).

ANDREWARTHA, H. G., BIRCH, L. C.: The distribution and abundance of animals. Chicago: The University Press 1954.

BARTLETT, M. S.: The use of transformations. Biometrics 3, 39–52 (1947).

BLISS, C. I.: Statistics in biology: statistical methods for research in the natural sciences, vol. 2. New York: McGraw-Hill 1970.

BOX, G. E. P., COX, D. R.: An analysis of transformations. Journal of the Royal Statistical Society (B) 26, 211–243 (1964).

BOX, G. E. P., TIDWELL, P. W.: Transformation of the independent variables. Technometrics 4, 531–550 (1962).

BURLEIGH, J. R., EVERSMEYER, M. G., ROELFS, A. P.: Development of linear equations for predicting wheat leaf rust. Phytopathology 62, 947–953 (1972a).

BURLEIGH, J. R., ROELFS, A. P., EVERSMEYER, M. G.: Estimating damage to wheat caused by *Puccinia recondita tritici*. Phytopathology 62, 944–946 (1972b).

BURLEIGH, J. R., ROMIG, R. W., ROELFS, A. P.: Characterization of wheat rust epidemics by numbers of uredia and numbers of uredospores. Phytopathology 59, 1229–1237 (1969).

BUTT, D. J.: Apple powdery mildew (*Podosphaera leucotricha*): Epidemiology. Report of East Malling Research Station for 1967, pp. 36–37 (1968).

BUTT, D. J.: Apple powdery mildew (*Podosphaera leucotricha*): Epidemiology. Report of East Malling Research Station for 1968, pp. 34–35 (1969).

BUTT, D. J.: Apple powdery mildew (*Podosphaera leucotricha*): Epidemiology. Report of East Malling Research Station for 1969, p. 48 (1970).

BUTT, D. J.: Apple powdery mildew (*Podosphaera leucotricha*): Epidemiology. Report of East Malling Research Station for 1971, p. 116 (1972a).

BUTT, D. J.: Epidemiology of plant diseases: A commentary on the 1971 Advanced Study Institute. Review of Plant Pathology **51**, 635–638 (1972b).

COLE, J. S.: Powdery mildew of tobacco (*Erysiphe cichoracearum* DC.) IV. Conidial content of the air within infected crops. Ann. appl. Biol. **57**, 445–450 (1966).

COOK, W. C.: Studies on the flight of nocturnal Lepidoptera. Rep. St. Ent. Minn. No. 18, 43–56 (1921).

DIRKS, V. A., ROMIG, R. W.: Linear models applied to variation in numbers of cereal rust uredospores. Phytopathology **60**, 246–251 (1970).

DRAPER, N. R., SMITH, H.: Applied regression analysis. New York-London-Sydney: John Wiley and Sons 1966.

EFROYMSON, M. A.: In: Mathematical methods of digital computers (ed. A. RALSTON and H. S. WILF). New York: John Wiley and Sons 1962.

EVERSMEYER, M. G., BURLEIGH, J. R.: A method of predicting epidemic development of wheat leaf rust. Phytopathology **60**, 805–811 (1970).

EVERSMEYER, M. G., BURLEIGH, J. R., ROELFS, A. P.: Equations for predicting wheat stem rust development. Phytopathology **63**, 348–351 (1973).

GOLDBERGER, A. S.: Econometric theory. New York: John Wiley and Sons 1964.

GREGORY, P. H.: The multiple-infection transformation. Ann. appl. Biol. **35**, 412–417 (1948).

HAMAKER, H. C.: On multiple regression analysis. Statistica Neerlandica **16**, 31–56 (1962).

HURST, G. W.: Forecasting the severity of sugar beet yellows. Plant Path. **14**, 47–53 (1965).

JAMES, W. C., SHIH, C. S., HODGSON, W. A., CALLBECK, L. C.: The quantitative relationship between late blight of potato and loss in tuber yield. Phytopathology **62**, 92–96 (1972).

JENKYN, J. F., HIRST, J. M., KING, G.: An apparatus for the isolated propagation of foliar pathogens and their hosts. Ann. appl. Biol. **73**, 9–13 (1973).

JOHNSON, C. G.: Migration and dispersal of insects by flight. London: Methuen and Co. Ltd. 1969.

KERR, A., RODRIGO, W. R. F.: Epidemiology of tea blister blight (*Exobasidium vexans*). II. Spore deposition and disease prediction. Trans. Brit. Mycol. Soc. **50**, 49–55 (1967a).

KERR, A., RODRIGO, W. R. F.: Epidemiology of tea blister blight (*Exobasidium vexans*). IV. Disease forecasting. Trans. Brit. Mycol. Soc. **50**, 609–614 (1967b).

KERR, A., SHANMUGANATHAN, N.: Epidemiology of tea blister blight (*Exobasidium vexans*). I. Sporulation. Trans. Brit. Mycol. Soc. **49**, 139–145 (1966).

KRANZ, J.: Eine Analyse von annuellen Epidemien pilzlicher Parasiten. I. Die Befallskurven und ihre Abhängigkeit von einigen Umweltfaktoren. Phytopathol. Z. **61**, 59–86 (1968a).

KRANZ, J.: Eine Analyse von annuellen Epidemien pilzlicher Parasiten. II. Qualitative und quantitative Merkmale von Befallskurven. Phytopathol. Z. **61**, 171–190 (1968b).

KRANZ, J.: Eine Analyse von annuellen Epidemien pilzlicher Parasiten. III. Über Korrelationen zwischen quantitativen Merkmalen von Befallskurven und Ähnlichkeiten von Epidemien. Phytopathol. Z. **61**, 205–217 (1968c).

KRANZ, J.: Einige Voraussetzungen für die Planung und Durchführung von Feldversuchen in der Epidemiologie. Z. Pflanzenkrankh. **10**, 573–581 (1972).

LAPWOOD, D. H.: Observations on blight (*Phytophthora infestans*) and resistant potatoes at Toluca, Mexico. Ann. appl. Biol. **68**, 41–53 (1971).

LARSON, H. J., BANCROFT, T. A.: Sequential model building for prediction in regression analysis I. Ann. Mathematical Statistics **34**, 462–479 (1963).

LAST, F. T., EBBEN, M. H., HOARE, R. C., TURNER, E. A., CARTER, A. R.: Build-up of tomato brown root rot caused by *Pyraenochaeta lycopersici* Schneider and Gerlach. Ann. appl. Biol. **64**, 449–459 (1969).

MASSIE, L. B.: Modeling and simulation of southern corn leaf blight disease caused by race T of *Helminthosporium maydis* Nisik. & Miyake. Ph.D. thesis. Pennsylvania State University. (1973).

MASSIE, L. B., NELSON, R. R.: The use of regression analysis in epidemiological studies of southern corn leaf blight. Phytopathology 63, 205 (1973).

MASSIE, L. B., NELSON, R. R., TUNG, G.: Regression equations for predicting sporulation of an isolate of race T of *Helminthosporium maydis* on a susceptible male-sterile corn hybrid. Plant Dis. Reptr. 57, 730–734 (1973).

MOORE, P. G.: Regression as an analytical tool. Appl. Statistics 11, 106–119 (1962).

MOTT, D. G.: An analysis of determination in population systems. In: Systems analysis in ecology (ed. K. E. F. WATT) pp. 179–194. New York: Academic Press 1966.

NELSON, R. R., TUNG, G.: Influence of some climatic factors on sporulation by an isolate of race T of *Helminthosporium maydis* on a susceptible male-sterile corn hybrid. Plant. Dis. Reptr 57, 304–307 (1973).

PREECE, T. F.: Continuous testing for scab infection weather using apple rootstocks. Plant. Path. 13, 6–9 (1964).

ROYLE, D. J.: Infection periods in relation to the natural development of hop downy mildew *(Pseudoperonospora humuli)*. Ann. appl. Biol. 66, 281–291 (1970).

ROYLE, D. J.: Quantitative relationships between infection by the hop downy mildew pathogen, *Pseudoperonospora humuli*, and weather and inoculum factors. Ann. appl. Biol. 73, 19–30 (1973).

ROYLE, D. J., LIYANAGE, A. de S.: Downy mildew: Epidemiology. Annual report of the department of hop research. Wye College for 1972, p. 24 (1973).

ROYLE, D. J., THOMAS, G. E.: Analysis of relationships between weather factors and concentrations of air-borne sporangia of *Pseudoperonospora humuli*. Trans. Brit. Mycol. Soc. 58, 79–89 (1972).

SALLANS, B. J.: Interrelations of common root rot and other factors with wheat yields in Saskatchewan. Scientific Agriculture 28, 6–20 (1948).

SCHRÖDTER, H.: Methodisches zur Bearbeitung phytometeoropathologischer Untersuchungen, dargestellt am Beispiel der Temperaturrelation. Phytopathol. Z. 53, 154–166 (1965).

SCHRÖDTER, H., ULLRICH, J.: Untersuchungen zur Biometeorologie und Epidemiologie von *Phytophthora infestans* (Mont.) de By. auf mathematisch-statistischer Grundlage. Phytopathol. Z. 54, 87–103 (1965).

SCHRÖDTER, H., ULLRICH, J.: Eine mathematisch-statistische Lösung des Problems der Prognose von Epidemien mit Hilfe meteorologischer Parameter, dargestellt am Beispiel der Kartoffelkrautfäule *(Phytophthora infestans)*. Agricultural Meteorology 4, 119–135 (1967).

SNEDECOR, G. W., COCHRAN, G.: Statistical methods. Iowa State University Press 1967.

SNOW, G. A., FROELICH, R. C., POPHAM, T. W.: Weather conditions determining infection of slash pines by *Cronartium fusiforme*. Phytopathology 58, 1537–1540 (1968).

TALBOYS, P. W., WILSON, J. F.: Effects of temperature and rainfall on the incidence of wilt *(Verticillium albo-atrum)* in hops. Ann. appl. Biol. 66, 51–58 (1970).

TU, J. C., HENDRIX, W. J.: The summer biology of *Puccinia striiformis* in South-eastern Washington. II. Natural infection during the summer. Plant. Dis. Reptr 54, 384–386 (1970).

VAN DER PLANK, J. E.: Plant diseases: epidemics and control. New York: Academic Press 1963.

WATSON, M. A.: The relation of annual incidence of beet yellowing viruses in sugar beet to variations in the weather. Plant Path. 15, 145–149 (1966).

WATSON, M. A., HEALY, M. J. R.: The spread of beet yellows and beet mosaic viruses in the sugar-beet root crop. II. The effects of aphid numbers on disease incidence. Ann. appl. Biol. 40, 38–59 (1953).

WATSON, M. A., WATSON, D. J., HULL, R.: Factors affecting the loss of yield of sugar beet caused by beet yellows virus I. Rate and date of infection; date of sowing and harvesting. J. Agric. Sci. 36, 151–166 (1946).

WATT, K. E. F.: Mathematical models for use in insect pest control. Canadian Entomologist 93, supplement 19, 62 pp. (1961).

WATT, K. E. F.: The nature of systems analysis. In: Systems analysis in ecology (ed. K. E. F. WATT) pp. 1–14. New York: Academic Press 1966.

WILLIAMS, E. J.: Regression analysis. New York: John Wiley and Sons 1959.

WRIGHT, S.: The interpretation of multivariate systems. In: Statistics and mathematics in biology (ed. O. KEMPTHORNE et al.). Iowa State University Press 1954.

WRIGHT, S.: Path coefficients and path regressions: alternative or complementary concepts? Biometrics 16, 189–202 (1960).

Addendum: Since going to press a paper has appeared by SHEARER and ZADOKS in which MRA was used in a field study of the latent period of *Septoria nodorum* on wheat. (SHEARER, B. L., ZADOKS, J. C.: The latent period of *Septoria nodorum* in wheat. 2. The effect of temperature and moisture under field conditions. Neth. J. Plant Path. 80, 48–60 (1974)).

CHAPTER IV

Non-linear Disease Progress Curves

D. JOWETT, J. A. BROWNING and BLANCHE COURNOYER HANING

1. Introduction

This chapter is about mathematical models — formulae capable in some degree of describing natural events, usually by oversimplification. In particular, it is concerned with the process whereby collected data are approximated by some explicit mathematical function. We are of the opinion that there are two common attitudes towards this process. The more primitive is to consider the model simply as a means of fitting a line, a plane, or a hyperplane through a swarm of points to some optimum degree of closeness, commonly by minimizing the sum of squared deviations from the fitted function. The second, more sophisticated approach is to attempt to develop a function derived from some theory concerning the underlying natural processes which generated the data. The two approaches are not exclusive, for the second always leads to something like the first. But the first does not necessarily lead to the second, nor is there inherent in the first approach any guarantee of an improved understanding of natural phenomena.

In developing a model based upon underlying natural phenomena, it is not our intention to produce a model which fits the data better than all other models. It will usually be possible, in fact, to find a better-fitting model. Our criterion must be that the model we choose fits better than alternative models based upon competing theories about the processes which gave rise to the data.

It should be clear that this returns to the natural scientist the paramount responsibility for explaining and describing the data. Anybody who has been exposed to statistics courses will recall the impression that the statistical analysis of data consists of selecting from an array of available techniques—regression, analysis of variance, etc.—one into which the data could be forced. This is an example of technique ruling data, and in the days when the absence of computers made the difficulties of fitting any but the simplest models insuperable it was almost inevitable, but it is neither inevitable nor desirable today. However, in returning the power to select the model to the natural scientist, we also return the responsibility for selecting wisely.

2. Linear, Non-linear and Linearizable Models

A linear model (BUTT and ROYLE, p. 80ff.) consists of additive strings of terms of the form (known value × parameter). A typical example is the linear regression model

$$Y = a + bX. \tag{1}$$

The terms are $(1 \times a) + (X \times b)$, where 1 and X are the known values, while a and b are the parameters. Hence, the widely quoted requirement in regression that X be measured "without error". And of course if we "know" X, we also know $X^2, X^3, 1/X, \log X$, etc., so models of the form

$$Y = a + bX + cX^2, \tag{2}$$

$$Y = a + b/X \tag{3}$$

are also linear in a and b, as long as we preserve the polite fiction that we "know" the values of X.

Examples of non-linear models are the exponential and logistic

$$Y = ae^{bx}, \tag{4}$$

$$Y = \frac{\kappa}{1 + \beta e^{-at}}. \tag{5}$$

However, the possibilities for the development of such models are endless. We note that in these models parameters appear multiplied or divided by functions of other parameters, that is, they no longer appear as additive strings. It is characteristic of such models that, if we attempt to fit them by conventional least squares, the normal equations also are nonlinear, and not in general soluble. Such models, however, are fitted by least squares in one of two ways—by linearizing the model or by iteration.

Not all models can be linearized. The process is one of finding some function—logarithm, inverse—which when applied to both sides of the model produces an expression on the right which is linear in the parameters. For example, the exponential model can be linearized by taking logarithms of both sides

$$Y = ae^{bx}, \tag{6}$$

$$\ln Y = \ln a + bX. \tag{7}$$

But the logistic model cannot be directly linearized, without additional assumptions, and we therefore fit it iteratively. Such methods of fitting involve first guessing values of the parameters, whereupon algorithms exist which may produce corrections to the original guesses which will progressively reduce the sum of squared deviations of the observations from the fitted line. This requires a computer, and will generally work only if the initial guesses are fairly good.

Of course, it is possible to fit a *linearizable* model in this way. The exponential model can be so fitted, for example. Paradoxically, fitting by direct least squares and by least squares after linearization will not produce the same parameter values. There are criteria which might lead us to prefer one technique or the other, but they need not be considered here. A more detailed discussion of linear models and their relation to non-linear models can be found in KEMPTHORNE (1952). For an excellent description of the potential of linear and linearizable models, see DANIEL and WOOD (1971).

3. The Derivation of Models from Differential Equations

BOX (1954) referred to polynomial models as mathematical French curves. This is because of their remarkable capacity to take upon an enormous range of shapes. Together with the ease with which they can be fitted, this has made them the approximations of choice for generations of scientists. They have been used for centuries to construct nautical tables. They are used in computing today to approximate transcendental functions. But as models they bear no relation to the phenomena they describe. (Exceptions to this are straight line models in one or many variables.) They are simply techniques for drawing a line through a set of points, and they do it very well. If we include segmented polynomials as a possibility, they will quite probably do better than any other model.

Non-linear models offer far more versatility in relation to underlying natural processes. Many examples could be quoted—probit analysis, Poisson models in bio-assay, etc.—but our concern here is with growth models derived from differential equations describing growth rates. The simplest such model is the exponential

$$\dot{y} = \frac{dy}{dt} = ay \tag{8}$$

where $\dot{y}$, or $\frac{dy}{dt}$ is the *rate of change* of y, or the amount whereby y changes in an extremely short interval of time. Such an equation is best understood intuitively in relation to micro-organisms reproducing by fission in an unlimited environment. Over an interval of time, the increase in the population will be equal to some constant, times the number present at the beginning of that interval. Thus, if there were ten to start with, and the time interval was long enough for the population to double, we will have twenty, an increase of ten. If, however, there were 100 to begin with, then after the same time interval we will have 200, an increase of 100. Such reasoning is elemental to biologists, and while mathematicians recognize that this situation, involving integer values only, gives rise to a slightly different kind of equation called a difference equation, it is closely approximated by the differential equation for large numbers. Mathematicians then show that the equation relating y itself to t is

$$y = be^{at}. \tag{9}$$

This is exponential growth which the environmentalists remind us cannot be sustained.

But Verhulst many years ago modified this equation to incorporate the concept of a limit to growth. He wrote

$$dy/dt = ay(b - y). \tag{10}$$

Now, b represents the upper limit of growth, the sum total of what the environment will support. If y is close to zero, then $(b - y)$ becomes very close to b, and the differential equation becomes effectively

$$dy/dt = aby. \tag{11}$$

The population is growing exponentially without constraint, with ab replacing a in the earlier equation. But as y, the size of the population, approaches b, the limiting size, then $(b - y)$ becomes very close to zero; this means that $ay(b - y)$ becomes close to zero, or growth virtually ceases.

What Verhulst incorporated into the model is the idea of "feedback". As the population grows larger, the information that it is approaching its limit is fed back into the system, slowing down growth and ultimately inducing a steady state. The equation that results, describing y in terms of t, is the logistic

$$y = \frac{\kappa}{1 + \beta e^{-at}}. \tag{12}$$

There is nothing remotely new in this. More detailed accounts may be found, in descending order of mathematical sophistication, in PIELOU (1969), PATTEN (1971) or ODUM (1971). We explain it in such detail only because of our belief that the very important logistic model is not commonly appreciated by biologists. The importance lies, in part, in the considerable capacity for these equations to be further modified. To illustrate this, let us digress.

4. Differential Equations and Ecology

There has been an upsurge of interest in ecological modeling in recent years, and much of this is carried out in terms of modification of Verhulst's basic equation. Consider two species in competition for the same resource base, and let y_1 and y_2 represent the amounts of each. Then we write

$$\frac{dy_1}{dt} = a_1 y_1 (b - c_1 y_1 - c_2 y_2), \tag{13}$$

$$\frac{dy_2}{dt} = a_2 y_2 (b - d_1 y - d_2 y_2). \tag{14}$$

In these equations, b represents again the carrying capacity of the environment, which is reduced by the amounts of *both* y_1 and y_2 present. It turns out that both species cannot co-exist, which is the basis for the principle of competitive exclusion, one of the most important generalizations in ecology.

Further, consider the situation of a host/parasite system where H denotes the amount of the host present and P denotes the amount of parasite.

$$\frac{dH}{dt} = a_1 H (b_1 - c_1 P), \tag{15}$$

$$\frac{dP}{dt} = a_2 P (-b_2 + c_2 H). \tag{16}$$

This may be less clear, but it indicates that the rate of growth of the host is decreased as the amount of the parasite increases, while the rate of growth of the parasite is increased by greater amounts of the host. The important thing is that b_1 and b_2 represent the carrying capacity of the environment.

Both of these are examples of *linked* equations describing biological *systems* and incorporating *feedback*. A final modification is to incorporate delay in the feedback, which can readily be done in computer simulations, often with catastrophic consequences to the behavior of the modeled populations. Again, the reader is refered to PIELOU (1969), ODUM (1972) or PATTEN (1971) for a more detailed account. The ultimate in this type of modeling is the computer simulation model, but we will defer until later a discussion of the relationship of our work to this type of model.

5. Logistic Models of Epidemics

The mathematical description of epidemics has a long history. FARR (1840) analyzed smallpox deaths in England, but only since the beginning of this century have models incorporating specific mechanisms of spread been developed. BAILEY (1957, 1967) reviewed much of this literature, and in the later work he states, during an epidemic, the rate of appearance of new cases characteristically increases rapidly to begin with, rises to a maximum, and falls way to zero, producing a curve which typically shows a bell-shaped distribution of new cases over time. If this distribution is accumulated, so that it represents total cases rather than new cases, a rising S-shaped curve will result.

Most models have been concerned with epidemics in animal and human populations, where the unit of observation is the diseased individual, and recovery leading to subsequent immunity is common. In plants, however, the diseased individual is not in itself of much interest, except in some perennials, and recovery does not lead to immunity. In epiphytotics, the total amount of disease present is the critical factor, for this represents the total photosynthetic area lost and metabolic products diverted.

VAN DER PLANK (1963) synthesized the literature on field crop diseases. He adopted simple exponential and logistic models to describe the development of epidemics, realizing as he did so that these models, like all models, represented an oversimplification of the complex processes involved. His units of measurement were the percentage of photosynthetic area lost in the crop, or as it is sometimes expressed, percentage infection as judged subjectively in diseased fields. That this is a crude technique of measurement does not, of course, detract from the value of the great insight which Van der Plank has achieved. But the technique is, at best, objective, and can be difficult to apply in some circumstances. JAMES and SHIH (1973) caution against equating incidence (percent leaves infected) with severity (percent leaf area affected) for powdery mildew and leaf rust on wheat. Furthermore, it requires the observer to walk through the field, and even handle the plants, thus disturbing the natural progress of the epidemic. A major advantage of the method is that, because the maximum disease is known to be 100 percent, it makes the logistic linearizable by the logit transformation.

We have applied logistic models to data obtained during artificially induced epidemics of *Puccinia coronata* Cda. var. *avenae* Fraser and Ledingham in small plots of oats (*Avena sativa* L.) where the progress of the disease was measured using spore density data obtained by Rotorod spore samplers located outside the plot. This method of estimation is objective and does not disturb the crop, but it is very susceptible to environmental fluctuations. Nevertheless, after suitable treatment, very good fits to logistic models can be obtained, without transformation of the data, and these logistic models can be parameterized in epidemiologically interesting and meaningful ways.

The attribution of the initial description and naming of the logistic growth curve to Verhulst in the early 19th century is due to YULE (1925). When a population is growing in a limited area, the rate of growth must tend to get less as the population grows, for the area into which it can expand is diminished by that growth. As previously explained, this is simply described mathematically by the differential equation:

$$\frac{dy}{dt} = ay(b - y) \tag{17}$$

where $\frac{dy}{dt}$ is the rate of growth, y is the size achieved, b is the maximum size achievable and a is a rate parameter.

Solving the first equation for t, we get:

$$t = \frac{1}{a} \int \frac{1}{y(b-y)} dy = -\frac{1}{ab} \ln\left(\frac{b-y}{y}\right) + c \tag{18}$$

where c is a constant of integration. Solving this for y yields an equation describing total growth as a function of time:

$$y = \frac{b}{1 + e^{abc} e^{-abt}} = \frac{\kappa}{1 + \beta e^{-\alpha t}} = F(t) \tag{19}$$

where

$$\kappa = b \qquad\qquad b = \kappa$$

$$\beta = e^{abc} \qquad\qquad a = \frac{\alpha}{\kappa}$$

$$\alpha = ab \qquad\qquad c = \frac{\ln \beta}{\alpha}.$$

This equation is written in various forms by different authors, and we also shall change its form. But essentially it describes an ascending S-shaped curve with respect to time, representing the *total* growth achieved. For the remainder of this discussion we will consistently use capital letters, Y and $F(t)$, to distinguish *total growth* from *growth increment*, which we will represent by lower case letters, y and $f(t)$. In this formulation of the logistic equation, α represents the rate parameter for growth when the population is very small, and β represents the maximum size to which the population can grow.

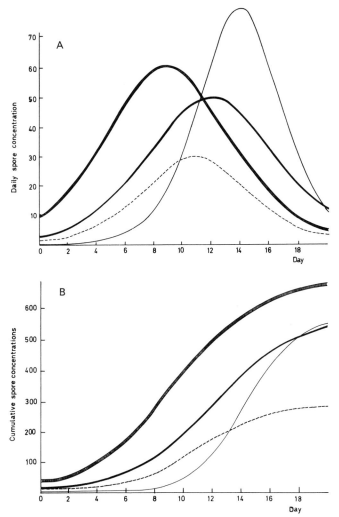

Fig. 34A and B. Typical logistic curves. (A) cumulative logistics, $F(t)$, (B) logistic rate curves. Parameter values in terms of $(M, u, \varkappa)$ are $(60, 5, 700)$, $(650, 8, 600)$, $(80, 10, 600)$, $(30, 7, 300)$ for solid, thin solid, broken dots and stippled lines respectively

For our purposes we also wish to define an equation to describe the rate of growth, or growth increment, in terms of the parameters α, β and $\varkappa$. We shall call this y, or $f(t)$.

$$f(t) = \frac{dF(t)}{dt} = \frac{\alpha\beta\varkappa e^{-\alpha t}}{[1 + \beta e^{-\alpha t}]^2}.\tag{20}$$

This equation describes a bell-shaped curve with respect to time. Typical curves of $F(t)$ and $f(t)$ are shown in Fig. 34.

It is instructive to compare the model with VAN DER PLANK's (1963) parametrization of the S-shaped epidemic curve. If we regard the maximum size to which the population can grow as 1.0, which is essentially what is being done when disease is estimated as a proportion, we can substitute 1.0 for b, and we get:

$$Y = F(t) = \frac{1}{1 + e^{ac}e^{-at}} \frac{1}{1 + ve^{-at}} \tag{21}$$

Re-arranging this, we can get:

$$\frac{Y}{1-Y} = \frac{1}{v} e^{at} \tag{22}$$

and this form is linearizable by taking $\log_e$ of both sides:

$$\ln \frac{y}{1-y} = -\ln v + at. \tag{23}$$

This is called the logit transformation, and is essentially what Van der Plank uses. He renames the parameter a as r, which corresponds to our parameter α. But of course they are not directly comparable, because while his curves are rising towards an asymptote of unity, ours are growing towards an asymptote which is not limited in this way.

   In practice, to facilitate examination of the model in terms more meaningful to plant pathologists, we have preferred to reparametrize the model as follows:

$$\mu = \frac{\ln \beta}{\alpha} = \text{time at which maximum growth occurs}$$

$$M = \frac{\alpha \kappa}{4} = \text{rate of growth at time } \mu$$

$$\kappa = \kappa = \text{maximum attainable growth}$$

   In terms of spore concentrations, these parameters will indicate the time when maximum spore release occurs, the spore concentration at this time, and some measure of the total accumulated spore release during the course of the epidemic.

6. Application of the Logistic Model to Spore Count Data

Full details of the experimental techniques involved in data collection are given in COURNOYER (1970). Briefly, isolated 50×50 foot plots of oats were inoculated at an appropriate stage with crown rust. After a period during which the epidemic was left to develop, the spore population was sampled for two hours daily using a Rotorod sampler adjacent to, and down wind from, the center of each plot. From the spore counts obtained, daily aerial spore concentrations were computed.

   For the purposes of our model, we regard the spore concentrations on any day, t_i, as a measure of the recent growth increment of the fungus, y_i. We visualize the fungus as advancing in a diffuse fashion through a fixed volume of host tissue. Sporulation represents the culmination of this growth for some limited region of the substrate, and the aerial spore concentration will be related in a simple linear fashion to the amount of substrate recently colonized, subject of course to error. The recent growth will be represented statistically under our model as:

$$y_i = f(t_i) + e_i . \tag{24}$$

The structure of the error deviations, e_i, is complex, being affected by both current and earlier climatic conditions. They cannot be regarded as following a normal distribution, nor indeed any distribution with constant variance, for their size will certainly be related to the size of y_i. We therefore expected, and observed, wide fluctuations of y_i from the postulated model, and so we examined simple data-smoothing devices, commonly called linear filters in time-series analysis. Many sophisticated devices are described under this heading by BOX and JENKINS (1970), but we simply took 2- and 3-day running averages, and accumulated the data. An example of the application of these techniques is given in Fig. 35. The accumulated data we regard as estimating total fungal growth, Y_i, and we represent this using $F(t) + e_i$.

The smooth shape of the accumulative curves is impressive, and initially we attempted to linearize this curve by accepting the final cumulative total spore count as an estimate of κ, and expressing earlier values as proportions of this. We transformed the resulting Y_i using the logit transformation, $\ln\left(\dfrac{Y}{1-Y}\right)$, and plotted against time. This gave us inverted S-shaped curves, as exemplified in Fig. 36, rather than the expected straight line. BURLEIGH, ROMIG and ROELFS (1969) tried a similar technique to characterize wheat rust epidemics, and while their data show more scatter than ours, some indication of non-linearity can be detected in their plots. Inverted S-shaped curves also occur in VAN DER PLANK (1963) when percentage disease is estimated and transformed similarly, for example the response of the variety "Voran" to potato blight illustrated on his p. 185.

Non-linear estimation is a rapidly growing area of statistics. Believing that the failure to obtain a straight line could be due to the faulty estimation of κ, we proceeded to fit $F(t)$ by non-linear methods, trying several techniques. DRAPER and SMITH (1968) have a good discussion of non-linear fitting, and they divide the techniques into (1) linearization procedures, (2) steepest descent procedures and (3) compromise procedures. All are iterative, and require that initial guesses of the parameter values be provided, which are modified in subsequent iterations to converge on the values of best fit. Success depends largely on getting good initial guesses, and fortunately PEARL and REED (1920) have described a simple technique for getting initial values of the parameters of the logistic curve which we found to be almost always successful. The technique of fitting we finally used is the modified Gauss-Newton, a compromise procedure described by HARTLEY (1961) and implemented for the IBM 360 by ATKINSON (1966) as TARSIER.

Several problems encountered in fitting the data are worth noting. In accumulating data, spores released before collection began are unaccounted for. Because counting began early in the epidemic, we believe this to be insignificant. More troublesome is missing data from the days, happily infrequent in our data, when heavy rain precluded spore collection. The inclusion of zero spores for a day does upset the accumulation of data, so we tried several methods of estimating values for

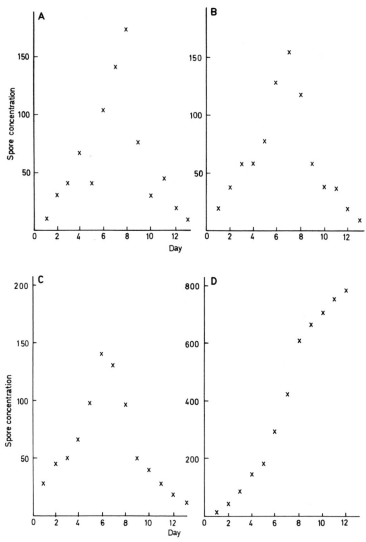

Fig. 35 A–D. Data plots of daily spore concentrations against day in an artificially induced crown rust epiphytotic (A) raw data, (B) two-day running averages, (C) three-day running averages, (D) accumulated spore concentrations

missing days. The simplest was to average the preceding and following days, but we also tried several techniques of fitting the curve $f(t)$ to the actual daily spore concentrations, and obtaining an estimate by evaluating $f(t)$ for the missing day. These may be termed linear and non-linear interpolation respectively. Linear interpolation we thought unsatisfactory because of the wide day-to-day fluctuations in spore concentration, which could lead to very poor estimation. Non-linear interpolation was more satisfying but very tedious, and so in most cases we inserted zero for the spore concentration for the rare missing days on the grounds that a worst it would not be much less accurate than any other method.

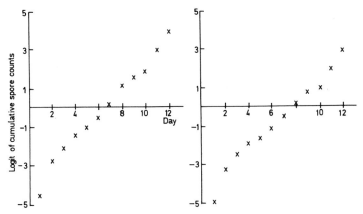

Fig. 36. Data plots obtained when accumulated daily spore counts are expressed as a proportion of final cumulative spore counts and subjected to logit transformation

Another problem is the lack of independence of the deviations from the model, inevitable in any simple smoothing procedure. We attempted to use the non-linear fitting procedure on the unsmoothed daily spore counts using the model $f(t)$. But this introduces another problem, in that the deviations of daily spore counts from the model are inherently dependent on the size of the spore counts. It was much harder to get convergence, and the observations around maximum spore releases were particularly erratic and seemed to us to influence unduly the shape of the fitted curve. We attempted to overcome this problem by taking logarithms of both sides, fitting

$$\ln y_i = \ln f(t_i) + e_i^*. \tag{25}$$

This stabilized the error, but led to very poor fits when the model was detransformed and plotted with the original data.

After intensive examination we therefore returned to our simple, initial procedure, accumulating daily spore counts, neglecting missing data and fitting cumulative logistic equations. Examples of such fitted curves are given in Fig. 37. The experiments were intended to compare treatments, and were usually replicated. Our basic strategy was not to calculate standard errors and make tests on parameters, but to obtain good estimates of the biologically meaningful parameters M, μ and κ for each plot individually, and subsequently to submit these parameter estimates to statistical analysis using conventional statistical techniques.

7. Other Suggested Growth Models

Many other growth models have been suggested and tried, but these are invariably extensions or modifications of the logistic model. Some examples are:

a) Monomolecular growth

This model is derived from the differential equation

$$\frac{dy}{dt} = k(A - y) \tag{26}$$

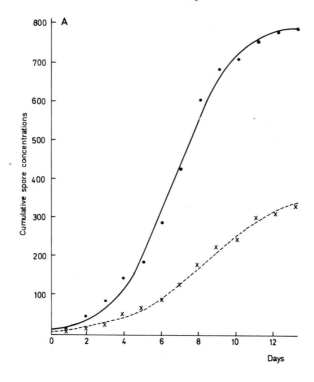

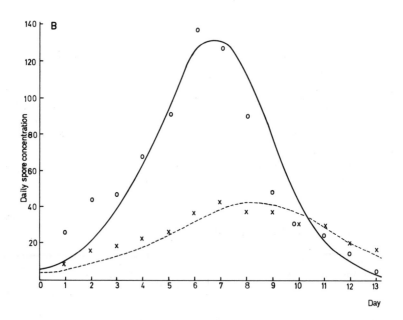

Fig. 37 A and B. Observed and fitted values, logistic curve fitted to cumulative data. (A) cumulative curves, (B) rate curve with 3-day running averages

or, in integrated form

$$y = A(1 - be^{-kt}) . \tag{27}$$

The function describes a situation where the rate of growth again declines as the population approaches its asymptote, but in this case the growth rate is *not* dependent on the amount of the organism present. VAN DER PLANK (1963) uses the model, calling it a simple interest model as contrasted to the compound interest assumption of the logistic. Substituting unity for the asymptote A, as van der Plank invariably does, the model implies

$$\frac{1}{1-y} = \frac{1}{b} e^{kt} \tag{28}$$

or

$$\ln \frac{1}{1-y} = -\ln b + kt . \tag{29}$$

Such a function might be appropriate where infection is begun by a very large amount of inoculum, without subsequent spread from the initial infections. A recent example of the application of this model to footrot of wheat is given by ROWE and POWELSON (1973).

b) Gompertz function

This model derives from the differential equation

$$\frac{dy}{dt} = k y \ln\left(\frac{A}{y}\right) = k y (\ln A - \ln y) . \tag{30}$$

The second form clearly indicates its relationship with the logistic, if we think of A as the asymptote towards which the population is growing. Once again, as y approaches A growth will cease, but in this case the rate at which growth is being slowed is not linear, but is itself slowing down as y approaches the asymptote. Compared with the logistic, early growth is faster and later growth slower.

The integrated form of the equation is

$$Y = Ae^{-be^{-kt}} \tag{31}$$

c) Richards function

$$\frac{dy}{dt} = \frac{ky}{nA^n} (A^n - y^n) \tag{32}$$

or

$$Y = A(1 + be^{-kt})^{-1/n}, \quad n > 0 , \tag{33}$$

$$Y = A(1 + be^{-kt})^{1/n}, \quad -1 < n < 0. \tag{34}$$

This is again a generalization of the logistic, suggesting much more complicated ways for the feedback mechanism to operate in slowing down the rate of growth. It was suggested by RICHARDS (1959) as a particularly realistic model of plant and animal growth (Table 2).

d) Time-dependent asymptote

TURNER et al. (1969) discussed the situation where the asymptote is itself a function of time

$$\frac{dy}{dt} = ay(k(t) - y) \tag{35}$$

where

$$k(t) = \frac{k}{(1 + e^{-mt})^{1/m}}.$$

This indicates that the asymptote, $k(t)$, is changing through some growth process which is itself logistic. This formulation is particularly appealing to students of the growth of human populations, for the obvious reason that the carrying capacity of the human environment clearly has changed over time, although it cannot continue to do so. It also has an obvious appeal as a model for epidemics in growing crops. The crop, which represents the potential limit to the growth of the fungal population, is itself growing logistically, as brought out, for example, by BERGER (1973). But the integrated form of the equation is particularly complex, which severely limits its analytic usefulness, and is not given here.

8. Epidemic Models for Animal Populations

The oldest work on epidemic growth curves is in human populations, where it was realized very early that the progress of an epidemic, as measured by total cases reported, usually followed an S-shaped curve, leading researchers to fit logistic models. However, it is important to recognize that an influenza epidemic is rather different from a rust epidemic. Influenza is contracted by individuals, whereas in most cases there seems little purpose in recognizing infected plants as individuals. After a short incubation period, the influenza patient can infect other susceptible individuals, but then he ceases to be infective, and he is removed from the population of susceptibles, for he is now immune.

A very simple deterministic model for this situation is given by BAILEY (1967) as

$$\frac{\Delta x}{\Delta t} = -\beta xy \tag{36}$$

where x = no. of infectives and y = no. of susceptibles at time t, β is the constant of mixing, and Δx represents the change in x during the short time interval Δt. (The change from dx and dt to Δx and Δt indicates that Bailey is using a model involving discrete time intervals, and integer values of x, in contrast to our continuous time models. The distinction is important, but involves somewhat sophisticated mathematics. Equations dealing with discrete time intervals are called difference equations, rather than differential equations, and for large values of x they are adequately represented by differential equations.)

It is not immediately apparent that this is the logistic equation in disguise, but it is. If we say that the initial population consists of $n+1$ individuals (n susceptible and 1 infected person), then at any given time, y, the number of susceptibles equals $n+1-x$, recalling that after infection individuals are immune. So we get

$$\frac{\Delta x}{\Delta t} = \beta x (n+1-x) \tag{37}$$

which is virtually the same as the logistic, with $(n+1)$ replacing b as the asymptote.

However, this model is inadequate for animal populations because it takes no account of the element of chance in transmitting infection. The number of people a person meets in the infectious phase will follow a Poisson distribution. It may be 0, 1, 2, etc., with a fixed probability for each. Then he may or may not transmit the disease, and this is a binomial variable. When many infectives are circulating freely, these random fluctuations will average out, but in the early stages of an epidemic they can be crucial. The first individual infected may simply walk around and, by chance, infect nobody, and thus avert an epidemic. Similar chance events can very much modify the rate of growth of the epidemic in its early stages. This makes the models of animal epidemiologists very much more complex, and requires estimates of the appropriate binomial and Poisson parameters.

Epidemiologists have also considered the effect of the lag or incubation period between becoming infected and becoming infectious in their models. Such lags have also been incorporated in some epidemic models, notably by LEONARD (1969) and WAGGONER et al. (1969, 1972). This is certainly a very promising field, but it is probably more important in the type of modeling that we are discussing to account for the effects of climate on the processes of infection.

9. Computer Simulation Models

The type of model we have been describing can be simulated on digital computers directly from the differential equation. The exponential model

$$\frac{dy}{dt} = ay \tag{38}$$

can be re-written by the usual rules of algebra as

$$dy = a\,y\,dt. \tag{39}$$

In words, this says the change in y over a small period of time (dy) equals a constant (a) times y times the small interval of time (dt). A digital computer, by its nature, operates in finite jumps, which we can make as small as we wish. Let us make the jump in time (dt) equal to .001 days. Then we initialize y at time zero to some value y_0, and the value at y_1 will be the value at y_0 plus the incremental change in y

$$y_0 = y_0$$
$$y_1 = y_0 + ay_0\,(0.001)$$
$$y_2 = y_1 + ay_1\,(0.001)$$
$$\vdots$$
$$y_t = y_{t-1} + ay_{t-1}\,(0.001).$$

This requires the computer to perform many repeated calculations, but of course that is what computers are for. Having obtained successive values of y, from y_0 to y_t, they can be plotted against t, and an exponential curve will result. Actually, the curve is only an approximation to the exponential, but mathematical techniques exist to modify the simple procedure outlined to make this as good an approximation as we wish. A good account of this, including some discussion of analog, as opposed to digital, computing, is given in PATTEN (1971).

The logistic is a little more complicated, incorporating the concept of negative feedback

$$y_0 = y_0$$
$$y_1 = y_0 + ay_0\,(b - y_0)\,(0.001)$$
$$y_2 = y_1 + ay_1\,(b - y_1)\,(0.001)$$
$$\vdots$$
$$y_t = y_{t-1} + ay_{t-1}\,(b - y_{t-1})\,(0.001)\,.$$

It is possible in the computer to delay this feedback, by incorporating into the algorithm the term $(b - y_{t-m})$ instead of the term $(b - y_{t-1})$, where y_{t-m} is the stage of growth achieved at some earlier stage than that immediately preceding, i.e. m steps back in the process. In studying epidemics, a reason for incorporating delay in the feedback would be the known interval between infection and the release of spores for reinfection. The pioneer in modeling complex systems in this fashion was FORRESTER (1961), who invented a language DYNAMO for the purpose, and the ultimate extension of the process seems to be the work of MEADOWS et al. (1972), whose "Limits to Growth" model, produced under the auspices of the Club of Rome, has generated such heated controversy in recent years.

The simulation described here is of very simple equations, of the kind we have used to model epidemics. It is possible to break down the process of disease spread into many steps, estimating parameter values at each step by very careful experiment, and incorporating into the model climatic effects, and indeed everything known to affect the disease process. Each step is then simulated in the computer by systems of linked equations. This has been achieved in the EPIDEM and EPIMAY models of WAGGONER et al. (1969, 1972), and produces an infinitely more complex and realistic process of disease modeling than we have achieved, and which it would be difficult to praise too highly. Our purpose here is to indicate how such simulation models grow out of the same kind of assumptions as we have made. We have approached the problem from the other end—first obtain the data, and then fit a suitable model, estimating appropriate parameters. Such an approach does enable comparisons to be made among epidemics, as we have done, but it is not predictive of the course of future epidemics, although it probably will predict relative rates of spread.

ZADOKS (1971) has attempted a distinction between two types of models, which he follows DE WIT (1968) in calling explicative and demonstrative. He places the logistic model among the demonstrative models, pointing out that VAN DER PLANK (1968) considers the assumptions of the logistic rather arbitrary. In this he is undoubtedly wrong. Whatever model we produce contains degrees of arbitrariness, and any model is no more than an approximation to the natural situation. It is true that there is far more arbitrariness in the logistic model than in more complex models, but it often fits disease curves very well, and is based on an attempt, albeit vastly oversimplified, to model the actual disease process. Many other models can be regarded as extensions of the logistic, incorporating additional modifications and assumptions, but not all, as we will show in the next section.

10. Pollen Count Data—an Alternative Model[1]

It is perhaps possible to emphasize our approach to modeling epidemics by a brief consideration of a set of data, similarly collected, but relating to a quite different natural situation. Many meteorological stations obtain aerial pollen counts, comparable to the aerial spore counts previously described, during the hay fever season. We have obtained a set of such counts for Green Bay, Wisconsin, from August 13 to September 30, 1959. A superficial examination of the data reveals a very similar structure to that of the oat crown rust spores, and no doubt a logistic model would fit the data. But the processes which produced the data are quite different, and are not growth processes at all. The shape of the curve is due to the distribution of flowering dates of ragweed about some mean date, and the central limit theorem of statistics leads us to postulate that this distribution might well be normal. The usual form of the normal distribution found in textbooks is adjusted, or normalized, so that the area under the curve is 1.0. However, we do not wish to do this, for the area under the curve is in fact related to the total pollen released, an important parameter for characterizing the situation.

Once again, there are several ways of writing this model. The usual equation for the normal distribution is

$$f(x) = \frac{1}{\sigma\sqrt{2\pi}} e^{-(x-\mu)^2/2\sigma^2}. \tag{40}$$

The $1/2\pi$ is the normalizing constant which ensures that the area under the curve equals 1. A more general formulation is

$$f(x) = re^{-s(x-t)^2} \tag{41}$$

---

[1] We are grateful to Dr. FRITZ FISHBACH, of the University of Wisconsin Green Bay, for making available to us the data described in this section.

where t is a parameter of location, the day of maximum spore release,

s is a parameter of spread, the distance from the mean to the point of inflexion,

r is a parameter related to the area under the curve.

It turns out that this is a linearizable model; in fact, if we write

$$y = re^{-s(x-t)^2} \tag{42}$$

where y is the number of spores released, then

$$\ln y = \ln r - s(x-t)^2$$
$$= \ln r - st^2 + 2stx - sx^2 \tag{43}$$

which is of the form

$$\ln y = a + bx + cx^2. \tag{44}$$

So in fact, adopting a model where pollen release follows a normal distribution simply implies that the logarithm of pollen release follows a quadratic model. The parameters r, s and t are easily and uniquely obtained from the parameters a, b, and c.

$$r = e^{a + b^2/4c}$$

$$s = c$$

$$t = -b/2c.$$

In Fig. 38, daily pollen counts are shown, together with a fitted Gaussian curve. The actual data show a distinct bimodal character, with a pronounced dip in the pollen count at about the mode of the fitted curve. Apparently, we do not have a very good fit to the data. However, the fact that the basic model is linearizable enables us to add terms for daily climatic variables—temperature, humidity, rainfall, etc.—and still fit the model by the usual multiple regression techniques. In Fig. 39, we show the predicted pollen counts (solid line) and observed pollen counts (open circles) when this is done. The dip in the middle is clearly explicable to a large degree by climatic variation. We suspect that variation in daily spore counts could be similarly explained, but the task of incorporating such linear terms into a non-linear model is quite substantial. One possible approach, which we have not yet tried, is to fit the non-linear model and then attempt to fit climatic effects to the deviations of the data from that model.

There are circumstances in which this would be a suitable model for fungal spores, for example of epiphytes on trees, where the successful initiation of infection by a germinating spore in a particular season does not contribute to further spore release in that season. That is, we are not dealing with a growth process. Cumulative normal distributions have been used by Large (1945) to model *Phyto-*

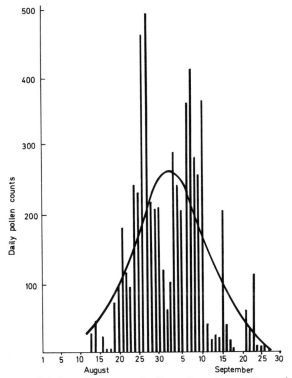

Fig. 38. Histogram of daily pollen counts in Green Bay, August–September 1959, with fitted Gaussian curve

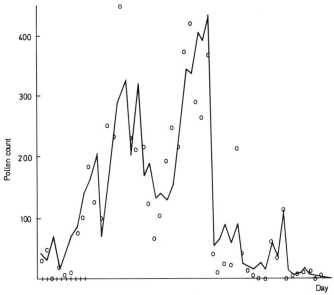

Fig. 39. Observed and predicted log pollen counts for Green Bay, August–September 1959, fitted Gaussian curve adjusted for climatic data. Open circles—observed pollen counts; solid lines—predicted pollen counts

phthera infestans, but this is not, in our estimation, a good thing to do. We would agree with ZADOKS (1971) that this is a demonstrative rather than explicative model when used in such circumstances. The important thing to remember is that the model should attempt to mirror, however imperfectly, the processes producing the data. Sometimes this will lead us to Gaussian curves, sometimes to logistic curves, but while both have similar shapes, and may in fact fit the data equally well, they will not both be reasonable models in the same set of circumstances.

11. Summary and Conclusions

We are trying to make two points in this paper. The first is that models of epidemics should be constructed to reflect the underlying natural processes, insofar as this is possible, and should not just be exercises in curve fitting. The second is that, for the spore count data we have examined, simple logistic models fit quite well, and can be parameterized in biologically meaningful ways. Furthermore, such models relate quite nicely to what is being done in other areas of biology. Ecologists are actively using linked differential equations, which derive from the logistic equation we have used, and logistic equations are the basis for much modeling in animal and human epidemiology, and also for the very exciting work being done in computer simulation of epidemics. In saying this, we are not claiming comparable sophistication for the models we have used. Our purpose has been to fit equations to data, not to simulate biological systems.

We have used only the simplest form of the logistic, and it seems to have been adequate for our purpose. There are more complex functions—the Gompertz function, the Richards function—and simpler functions such as the monomolecular. But if we examine the differential equations from which these quite different functions arise, and which model the growth processes which we believe are occurring, then we see that these are also modifications of the logistic, incorporating additional assumptions. VAN DER PLANK (1968) has also suggested additional restrictions on the logistic. The question of whether or not to make these additional assumptions is the crucial one in modeling data, but Occam's razor, which states that multiplicity ought not to be posited without necessity, or, as it is sometimes stated, the simplest explanation which fits the facts is the most acceptable, should incline us not to make them if the simple model fits.

We do not maintain that logistic models are suitable for all similar situations. We discuss a situation where in fact they are quite unsuitable because they fail to reflect underlying processes, even though the data are superficially similar. Nor do we believe that the disease progress curve is truly logistic, for any model can only be a pallid reflection of reality. Finally, we acknowledge that, in general, linearizable models are preferable, because of the ease with which extra terms can be added, to explain other sources of variation in the data. Finally, we would like to emphasize the pedagogical significance of the logistic and related functions. Students of epidemiology should certainly receive an intensive exposure to it at an early stage of their training.

The type of data we have used is ideally suited for investigation of the effects of climate on the spread of plant pathogens. It is a disadvantage of the logistic that it is not easily linearizable, but it is not a fatal disadvantage. Perhaps the deviations from fitted logistic curves can be used as dependent variables in linear equations fitting climatic effects.

The most important thing about any model is that it should be useful. For certain purposes, polynomial models might be preferable, particularly if applied to the logarithms of daily spore counts, with additional terms added to the model for climatic variables. Such models do not reflect the reality of the situation, but may help to understand phytopathological processes. Any model is just a way of looking at data. There are limited advantages to be obtained by non-biologists looking at biological data, and so perhaps in the end the most important thing is that the biologist should know his model, understand his purpose in using it, and extract from it every milligram of information that it contains.

References

ATKINSON, J. D.: TARSIER reference manual. Iowa State University Statistical Laboratory, Numerical Analysis-Programing Series, No. 8 (1966).

BAILEY, N. T. J.: The mathematical theory of epidemics. London: Griffin 1957.

BAILEY, N. T. J.: The mathematical approach to biology and medicine. New York: John Wiley and Sons 1967.

BERGER, R. D.: *Helminthosporium turcicum* lesion numbers related to numbers of trapped spores and fungicide sprays. Phytopathology **63**, 930–933 (1973).

BOX, G. P.: The exploration and exploitation of response surfaces: some general considerations and examples. Biometrics **10**, 16–60 (1954).

BOX, G. P., JENKINS, G. M.: Time series analysis. San Francisco, Cambridge, London, Amsterdam: Holden-Day 1970.

BURLEIGH, J. R., ROMIG, R. W., ROELFS, A. P.: Characterization of wheat rust epidemics by numbers of uredia and urediospores. Phytopathology **59**, 1229–1237 (1969).

COURNOYER, B. M.: Crown rust epiphytology, with emphasis on the quality and periodicity of spore dispersal from heterogeneous oat cultivar-rust race populations. Ph.D. Thesis, Iowa State University (1970).

DANIEL, C., WOOD, F. S.: Fitting equations to data. New York: Wiley-Interscience 1971.

DE WIT, C. T.: Theorie en model. Wageningen 1968.

DRAPER, N. R., SMITH, H.: Applied regression analysis. New York 1968.

FARR, W.: Progress of epidemics. Second Report of the Registrar General of England and Wales (1840).

FORRESTER, J. W.: Industrial dynamics. Cambridge, Mass.: MIT 1961.

HARTLEY, H. O.: The modified Gauss-Newton method for the fitting of non-linear regression functions by least squares. Techometrics **3**, 269–280 (1961).

JAMES, W. C., SHIH, C. S.: Relationship between incidence and severity of powdery mildew and leaf rust on winter wheat. Phytopathology **63**, 183–187 (1973).

KEMPTHORNE, O.: The design and analysis of experiments. New York: John Wiley and Sons 1952.

LARGE, E. C.: Field trials of copper fungicide for the control of potato blight I. Foliage protection by stem rust. Plant Dis. Reptr. **43**, 855–862 (1945).

LEONARD, K. J.: Selection in heterogeneous populations of *Puccinia graminis* f. sp. *avenae*. Phytopathology **59**, 1845–1850 (1969).

MEADOWS, D. H., MEADOWS, D. L., RANDERS, J., BEHRENS, W. W.: The limits to growth. New York: Universe Books 1972.

ODUM, E. P.: Fundamentals of ecology (3rd edition). Philadelphia, London, Toronto: W. B. Saunders 1971.

Patten, B.C.: A primer for ecological modeling and simulation with analog and digital computers. In: Systems Analysis and Simulation in Ecology (ed. B.C. Patten) vol. I, pp. 3–121. New York, London: Academic Press 1971.

Pearl, R., Reed, L.J.: On the rate of growth of the population of the United States since 1790, and its mathematical representation. Nat. Acad. Sci. Proc. 6, 275–288 (1920).

Pielou, E.C.: An introduction to mathematical ecology. New York: Wiley-Interscience 1969.

Richards, F.J.: A flexible growth function for empirical use. J. exp. Bot 10, 290–300 (1959).

Rowe, R.C., Powelson, R.L.: Epidemiology of Cercosporella footrot of wheat. Phytopathology 63, 984–988 (1973).

Turner, M.E., Blumenstein, B.A., Sebaugh, J.L.: A generalization of the logistic law of growth. Biometrics 25, 577–580 (1969).

Van der Plank, J.E.: Plant diseases: epidemics and control. New York, London: Academic Press 1963.

Van der Plank, J.E.: Disease resistance in plants. New York, London: Academic Press 1968.

Waggoner, P.E., Horsfall, J.G.: EPIDEM: a simulator of plant disease written for a computer. Conn. Agr. Exp. Sta. Bull 698 (1969).

Waggoner, P.E., Horsfall, J.G., Lukens, R.J.: EPIMAY: a simulator of Southern Corn Leaf Blight, Conn. Agr. Exp. Sta. Bull 729 (1972).

Yule, G.U.: The growth of populations and the factors which control it. J. Roy. Stat. Soc. 88, 1–58 (1925).

Zadoks, J.C.: Systems analysis and the dynamics of epidemics. Phytopathology 61, 600–610 (1971).

CHAPTER V

Simulation of Epidemics

P. E. WAGGONER

1. Introduction

Scientists can be distinguished from others who try to improve the human condition by their striving to understand thoroughly how something works. People in many pursuits work to control outcomes, while the scientist works to understand, often reducing a phenomenon to its parts, experimenting with the parts until they are understood, and then assembling understandings of the simpler parts into an understanding of the more complex whole. Therefore, mathematical simulation, which I conceive here as the logical assembly of knowledge of the interrelations among pathogen, host and weather for calculating the course of epidemics, can be placed in the center of plant pathology because it is an orderly, if trying, way of assembling our fundamental knowledge of the parts of epidemics into an understanding of whole epidemics. Although perfect knowledge and perfect simulation is beyond our grasp, we can already make good use of the fundamental pathology that we have in order to analyze, simulate and predict epidemics, to test the adequacy of present pathology, to be surprised sometimes at how well we do, and always to illuminate the importance or insignificance of lacunae in our knowledge.

The mathematical simulator that I am describing is superficially a program that causes a computer to ingest weather observations, digest them according to the tastes of the pathogen, and finally print numbers that mimic the growth of an epidemic; but to understand the simulator fully one needs to distinguish it from other methods of producing such numbers. The simulator differs from a logical differential equation, e.g. VAN DER PLANK'S (1963) proportionality between time and the relative change in disease in the explicit consideration by the simulator of, say, wind and spores or dew and appressoria. The simulator also differs from an accurate empirical regression, e.g. relation between rust and weather in the Great Plains in 1967–1970 (BURLEIGH et al., 1972), in the use of laboratory observations in the simulator and the pretension by the simulator to all regions and years. Believing, however, that specifics are more illuminating than generalities, I shall promptly turn to illustrating the nature of simulation in a particular disease.

2. An Introductory Example

ROYLE'S (1973) observations of quantitative relationships between infections by the hop downy mildew pathogen, *Pseudoperonospora humuli,* and weather and inoculum factors outdoors and his preceding study of the mildew in laboratory and garden (ROYLE, 1970) provide a wealth of data and analyses for comparison and trial of the three mathematical methods that I have just mentioned[2].

2.1 Analysis by Differential Equation

Beginning with the differential equation with its parameter of compound interest or of doubling time so well employed by VAN DER PLANK (1963), one can analyze the eruption of mildew in Royle's hop garden in the Mays of 1967 and 1968 by relating the logarithm of the percentage of leaves infected to time and quickly learn that the doubling time for infection was about 3 days in one year and 8 days in the other. A refinement on the simple proportionality between relative increase in infection and time is the so-called Bertalanffy equation, which ANALYTIS (1973) found fits the increase in apple scab closely and which makes the change in $\ln (1 - \sqrt{y})$ proportional to time where y is relative amount of disease. According to this equation, the doubling time for disease lengthens as the supply of healthy leaves decreases. Thus in the year when the doubling time seemed 3 days according to the simple exponential rule, it changes from about 3 days to double from 20% to 8 days to double from 40% according to the Bertalanffy equation. These two equations neatly summarize many observations in a few parameters and recognize that organisms multiply rather than add. The exercises also show that one year was worse than the other, but they have no place for results from the laboratory and are of little use in predicting the epidemic that would be called forth by the weather of another May.

2.2 Summary by Regression

Prediction, however, is exactly the purpose of the regression equations relating epidemic to weather that Royle estimated from observations in a garden in 1969, 1970, and 1971. Multiple regressions were estimated, 900 in all, by combining up to four independent variables such as the duration of rain or the spores in the air. Although the estimated parameters of the regression equations cannot easily be tested or interpreted in terms of fundamental knowledge of the pathogen, they do summarize countless observations, and Royle went on to the essential additional tasks of testing the equations in other years and reasoning about their success and failure in terms of fungal requirements. He went as far as possible with empirical analysis and then explained the limitations in terms that evoke a logical simulation model. His explanations of the limitations are worth repeating to set the stage for simulation.

In a specific example Royle wrote, "Large errors ... were encountered ... (in the prediction by regression) due to exceptionally great aerial spore catches in the absence of suitable wet conditions." In other words, he said that the empirical equation.

$$\text{disease} = a + b_1 \text{ (inoculum)} + b_2 \text{ (wet)}$$

---

[2] For another detailed discussion see BUTT and ROYLE.

explained about three-quarters of the variation in disease in one set of observations, but failed with another set because it was illogical. The illogic is the linear form of the regression equation, which says increased inoculum causes the same increase in disease whether the times are wet or not wet. His verbal analysis of the failure can be translated into a new equation where functions of inoculum and wet are multiplied—not added:

$$\text{disease} = f(\text{inoculum})\, g(\text{wet})$$

says wet cannot increase disease without inoculum and vice versa.

Still another limitation of the regression equation was illuminated when Royle stated, "Severe infection was sometimes underestimated mainly because the effects of sequences ... were not accommodated by the regression ..." He said, in effect, that whether spores arrived before or after a wet period logically made the difference between severe and no infection, but the regression equation and even the more logical equation above failed because they ignored the sequence of things and equated the effect of a million spores that alighted just before a rain, with a million that alighted and perished after the leaves had dried.

The necessary but illogical omission of sequence or order from a regression equation may significantly change the conclusions of analysis as well as limit the future use of the equation. Thus in one year the correlation between infection and aerial spore concentration was slight, but the correlation between infection and spores washed into a funnel by rain was great, suggesting that rain-borne were intrinsically more effective than air-borne spores. As Royle said, however, a logical explanation is simply "aerial dispersal was not commonly accompanied by optimum weather conditions for infection." If as I suspect "accompanied" means "followed", then a logical calculation that lets spores that arrive in dry weather wither and those that arrived just before wet weather prosper would remove the apparent difference between spores sucked in from the air versus those washed down by the rain.

In another example, Royle wrote "infection was overestimated ... because the rainfall was in excess of the range encountered when estimating the equation from the ... data." In other words, Royle said that the regression equation

$$\text{disease} = a + b_1 (\text{rain})$$

failed when the coefficient b_1 was empirically taken from the consequences of a moderately long rain and then multiplied by a very long rain, because logically a brief rain causes no infection, a long rain causes some infection, and a very long rain causes no more infection than a merely long one.

Further illumination is found in Royle's discussion of the paradoxical effectiveness of wet from rain versus ineffectiveness of wet from dew, a paradox that he coped with by simply omitting dew. The danger in this, as Royle suggested, is that the paradox arose from dew falling at night, rain falling during daylight, stomata being open only in light, and the pathogen entering only *via* stomata. Thus the empirically fitting but logically dangerous equation would likely fail if rain fell by night.

Again we see Royle using a regression equation as a concise summary of the relations between weather and epidemic in one or two years and then logically explaining its failure to fit the relations of another year.

2.3 Testing a Logical Equation for a Simulator

Having shown how deductions from phytopathological common sense, which were akin to building a logical simulator, were used by Royle to interpret the failure in predicting the events of, say, 1969 by a linear regression summarizing the events of 1968, I shall take the next step and try writing a logical equation that could be part of a simulator, at least for one step in the disease cycle. The method is common sense, keeping dimensions of time, length, etc. straight, and using ROYLE'S (1970) earlier observations of hop mildew in laboratory and garden. The outcome should be an equation that can be tested and interpreted in terms of fundamental knowledge. Since Royle observed moisture, air-borne spores, and subsequent infection of leaves in the garden, the material is at hand to write the relation between spores and disease without worrying about the production and dispersal of the spores. Avoiding this worry is a considerable advantage.

A logical equation is more easily written for D, the increase in proportion of leaf area diseased per day, rather than for the percentage of leaves infected. One may be translated into the other because the proportion of the leaf area diseased is about 0.16 to 0.40% of the proportion of leaves infected (ROYLE, 1973). It is logical to begin by relating the increase D to the number of spores caught on each m^2 of foliage, which is estimated from the product of several factors that should increase the spore catch: the S spores/m^3 of air, the U meters of air that pass during the deposition period of perhaps a day, and a deposition fraction P. More leaves will mean that the spores caught per m^2 of land are spread over more m^2 of foliage, and the leaf area index LAI will appear as a divisor. To obtain the number of infections from the spores/m^2 one must multiply by I, the number of infections per spore per hour integrated over the hours of the infection period. Finally, the number of infections must be translated into area of lesions per area of leaf by multiplying by A m^2 lesion per infection. The entire expression is:

$$D = (S \cdot U \cdot P/(LAI))\, I \cdot A \tag{1}$$

$$\text{dimensionless} = \frac{\text{spores}}{m^3} \cdot m \cdot \frac{\text{infection}}{\text{spore}} \cdot \frac{m^2}{\text{infection}}.$$

The form of the equation implies that spores are deposited before the infection period begins and that D is observed after the lesions have grown to A m^2. Since D, P, and LAI are dimensionless, the dimensions of the equation are correct, and the next step is seeing whether values of the parameters from the literature, especially Royle's observations, can be reconciled by Eq. (1).

The parameters are estimated from Royle's observations of May 12–21, 1967 infection weather and spore flight, which were followed in a week by 50% of the leaves or about 0.15% of the area infected:

Date	12	13	14	15	16	17	18	19	20	21
Spores/m^3	0	20	5	5	5	0	0	0	5	5
Weather	M	M	M	0	0	M	0	M	M	0

The symbol M for weather indicates a major infection period, which is more than 6 hours wet at a moderate temperature according to Royle's observations of duration of wetness required for leaf infection in controlled experiments. Only May 14 and 20 need concern us for the product of S and I are zero at other times except May 13, and on May 13 the spores arrived after the leaves had dried. Since the I were likely the same on the three days, the ratio of the 0.0015 sum of the D to the (5 + 5) spores per m^3 of air should equal the remaining parameters of Eq. (1):

$$0.0015/10 = U \cdot P \cdot I \cdot A/LAI. \tag{2}$$

Since Eq. (2) is logical and its parameters are identified with physical factors, the formulation can be tested by seeing whether reasonable values of the parameters produce 0.0015/10. Wind travel U during deposition is reasonably 10^4 m or about 0.3 miles per hour for a day, and a lesion area A of 1 cm^2 or 10^{-4} m^2 is reasonable. If LAI is 3, and P is 1/30 (GREGORY, 1961), then infection I per spore must be 0.0135 which means 1.3% of the deposited spores caused an infection during a major infection period. If we knew how many spores Royle applied during his controlled inoculation experiments, we could test the realism of the 1.3%, but for the present this percentage seems reasonable enough.

The equation can be tested further with the observations of 1968 when May 5 to 14 were followed in a week by an infection of 30% of the leaves or about 0.09% of the area. The observations were:

Date	5	6	7	8	9	10	11	12	13	14
Spores/m^3	10	15	0	0	2	1	8	70	2	100
Wheather	M	0	N	M	M	M	M	M	N	M

The symbol N for weather indicates a minor infection period, which controlled experiments had shown barely caused infection. Ignoring the few infections during N, ignoring the spores that arrived after leaves dried on May 5, 9, 12, and 14, adding the spore concentrations during the M periods of May 10 and 11, and following the procedure of Eq. (2), one arrives at a value of 0.0009/9 for the parameters in the right-hand member of Eq. (2) in 1968. This is about their value in 1967, and if the other parameters have the same values in the two years, then the infection rate I must have changed little. There was about 1 infection per hundred spores, a reasonable ratio, for two years. Now if infection dominates or is proportional to the increase in disease and Eq. (1) is valid as well as logical, it and the rough estimates of its parameters from 1967 and 1968 should agree with the regression equations that summarize the relation between spore concentration and subsequent infection during the following three years (ROYLE, 1973).

The regression equation for 1969–71 that explained 70% of the variation in the index of infection requires values for wetness, rainfall and air-borne spores during 48 h. I have assumed that wetness was 12 hours per day and rainfall was 3 mm per day. In 1967 and 1968 the average S spores/m^3 during the infection periods was about 5, and I have assumed that this same concentration of spores flew during three 48-hour periods of 1969–1971. Given these values, the regression of 1969–1971 estimates about 10% of the foliage infected per period or a total of about 30% after three 48-hour periods. Since this 30% derived from the regression equation for 1969–1971 equals the disease caused by the same number of spores in 1968, which was consistent with the logical Eq. (1), the logical equation agrees with all the experience summarized in the regression equation. A further test is comparing parameters of Royle's regression equation for the logarithm of infection to the change in the logarithm of D with change in S in Eq. (1). The derivative of the logarithm of D with respect to S in Eq. (1) is lge/S or 0.43/S, which is 0.08 when S is 5. This .08 is much larger than Royle's regression coefficients, which disagreement is attributed to the uncertainty in saying what S was in 1969–1971 and the different forms of Eq. (1) and a linear regression equation.

This example of a logical and an empirical equation has illustrated the power of the logical to use our fundamental knowledge of pathology and the power of the summary of experience in an empirical regression equation to test the logical.

Now let us turn to the limitations of the regression equation that Royle cited and see if the logical, simulation Eq. (1) would have done better. One failure was caused by adding inoculum and wetness rather than multiplying them, and Eq. (1) corrects this. Another failure was the ignoring of sequence by the regression equation, and I have skirted this issue by saying the S were deposited before wetness. A further failure was caused by disease not increasing linearly with rainfall, and Eq. (1) would do better if the infection parameter I followed Royle's observations of duration of wetness required for infection and increased from essentially zero with 2 hours of wet caused by rain on to a maximum after 6 hours. Finally, the regression equation evidently ignored nighttime dew sucessfully because most zoospores failed to settle on and penetrate stomata closed in the dark, and this has not been rectified in Eq. (1).

2.4 From Equation to Computer

A simulator will generally be a numerical integration or summing of disease increase on a digital computer, encompassing the entire life cycle of a pathogen. Equation (1) would be the portion of the simulator that related environment and spores in the air to subsequent infection. Previous calculations would have to calculate S, and later calculations would have to carry on to the later stages. If I now write the phenomena of Eq. (1) into a computer program, the slights of sequence and stomata can be rectified.

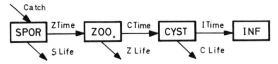

Fig. 40. A model of the catching of spores and their subsequent infection of foliage

The portion of the fungal cycle encompassed by the simulator is presented diagramatically in Fig. 40. The CATCH is the sporangia per hour caught per m² of foliage while the leaves are dry. These accumulate in a sum or integral denoted by the box SPOR. They die on the dry leaf, and an average life SLIFE of 3 h is reasonable (SONODA and OGAWA, 1972). When the foliage becomes wet, on the other hand, the sporangia produce zoospores ZOO in an average of ZTIME or about 2 h (ZATTLER, 1931).

The zoospores swim about and then may encyst on top of stomata where they can later infect the foliage (ROYLE and THOMAS, 1971a, 1971b). These effective individuals accumulate in the integral CYST after a CTIME of about 1/2 hour in the light or 2 h in the dark (ROYLE and THOMAS, 1973).

Many zoospores will not succed in encysting on a stoma, however, and will perish or encyst ineffectively between stomata after an average of ZLIFE hours. ZLIFE depends upon wetness of the spores. If they are dry, they will die in a ZLIFE of about 1/2 h according to D. J. Royle's unpublished estimate. If they are both wet and in the dark, three-quarters will not land on the closed stomata while one-quarter will, an outcome that implies ZLIFE is $^2/_3$ h or a third of the CTIME of 2 h for successful encysting on a stoma. Since only a quarter fail to find a stoma in the light, on the other hand, ZLIFE must be $^3/_2$ h or three times the CTIME of $^1/_2$ h in the light.

The encysted zoospores will perish if the foliage dries before they push germ tubes into stomata. Since the encysted zoospores seem more resistant than swimming ones, I made CLIFE 2 h. Finally some individuals will succeed, pushing a tube into a stoma after an average ITIME, which D. J. Royle estimates to be $^1/_2$ h. These successful infections accumulate in INF.

After this review of the biology of the catching and eventual infection, a simulator can be easily written in the computer language CSMP (IBM, 1969), which is specially devised to calculate integrals that grow with time. Thus the equation

$$SPOR = INTGRL\,(0., CATCH - RSDIE - RSGERM)$$

says that the integral SPOR sporangia/m² foliage increases from 0. at time 0. at a rate that is increased by CATCH and decreased by RSDIE and RSGERM.

Remembering the preceding discussion of deposition, I write

$$CATCH = S*U*P/LAI,$$

or the sporangia/m² foliage per hour CATCH is the product of the S sporangia per m³ of air, the wind U m per hour and the dimensionless deposition fraction P divided by the LAI m² of foliage per m² of land. In a numerical example, if a concentration of 10000 sporangia/m^2 passed over an LAI of 2 at a speed of 1 m/h and 1% were caught, the integral SPOR would be increased the following number of sporangia/m^2 per hour.

$$CATCH = 10000 * 1 * 0.01/2 = 50 .$$

Since the mortality rate RSDIE sporangia/m^2 per hour applies only when the leaves are dry, the equation contains a parameter DRY, which is 1 when leaves are dry and otherwise is 0. Because sporangia have an average life of SLIFE or 3 h, it is approximately[3] correct to say that 1/SLIFE or 1/3 of the sporangia die each hour.
Thus, the death rate of sporangia/m^2 per hour is

$$RSDIE = DRY * SPOR / SLIFE ,$$

or on a dry leaf holding 50 sporangia/m^2,

$$RSDIE = 1. * 50./3 .$$

If the SPOR were more fortunate because the leaf was wet, RSDIE would be 0, and SPOR would be depleted at a rate RSGERM of successful germination. Since the average time for zoospore formation is ZTIME or 2 h, the rate of germination of sporangia/m^2 per hour is:

$$RSGERM = WET * SPOR/ZTIME$$

WET is 1 or 0 according to whether the leaf is wet or dry. In a numerical example of 50 sporangia/m^2 on a wet leaf,

$$RSGERM = 1. * 50./2. = 25 .$$

The census or integral ZOO of zoospores/m^2 grows from an initial 0. according to

$$ZOO = INTGRL (0., RZOO - RZDIE - RCYST) .$$

Since approximately six zoospores are formed from each sporangium, the rate RZOO of zoospores formation per m^2 and per hour is

$$RZOO = 6. * RSGERM .$$

When 25 sporangia/m^2 germinate, 150 zoospores appear.
When wet, the zoospores become encysted on stomata in an average time CTIME, or

$$RCYST = WET * ZOO/CTIME$$

---

[3] Although the mortality rate is actually ln 2/SLIFE or 0.7/SLIFE, not 1/SLIFE, I have neglected the refinement of the 0.7 here and in following equations.

zoospores/m^2 become encysted on stomata per hour. CTIME varies with the light, being only $^1/_2$ h in the light, but fully 2 h in the dark. The command INSW in CSMP causes this choice to be made.

$$CTIME = INSW \, (LIGHT, 2., 0.5)$$

makes CTIME equal 2 when LIGHT is -1 and 0.5 when it is 1. In a numerical example, 150 zoospores/m^2 of leaf would form cysts on stomata at RCYST of 75 per hour in the dark and 300 per hour in the light. These rates could not, of course, be sustained long because of the depletion of ZOO, and the calculation would have to go by small time intervals, moving, e.g., 5 spores from ZOO to CYST in $^5/_{75}$ h or 4 min in the dark or in $^5/_{300}$ or 1 min in the light.

Mortality presents a similar problem of choosing a mean time. The swimming zoospores die or end ineffectively settled between stomata at RZDIE zoospores/m^2 per hour:

$$RZDIE = ZOO/ZLIFE .$$

The average life ZLIFE must be chosen according to both wetness and light. The mycological conclusions of an earlier paragraph can be summarized in a table of ZLIFE of $^1/_2$, $^2/_3$ or $^3/_2$ according to the environment:

	DARK	LIGHT
DRY	$^1/_2$	$^1/_2$
WET	$^2/_3$	$^3/_2$

The appropriate value is chosen from ZLIFE by a nest of INSW:

$$ZLIFE = INSW \, [WET - 0.5, 0.5, INSW \, (LIGHT, 0.7, 1.5)] .$$

The RCYST zoospores/m^2 per hour that successfully encyst on stomata increase the census CYST:

$$CYST = INTGRL \, (0., RCYST - RCDIE - RINF) .$$

On dry leaves they die with a CLIFE of 2 h:

$$RCDIE = DRY * CYST/CLIFE .$$

In an example, a population CYST of 150 encysted spores/m^2 resting on stomata would expire at

$$RCDIE = 1. * 150./2. = 75 .$$

encysted zoospores/m^2 per hour.

The successful individuals would increase the infections/m^2:

$$INF = INTGRL \, (0., RINF)$$

at a rate RINF that goes ahead when foliage is wet:

$$RINF = WET * CYST/ITIME.$$

Since this proceeds rapidly because ITIME is only $^{1}/_{2}$ h, 150 encysted spores/m^2 would cause

$$RINF = 1. * 150/0.5 = 300$$

or 5 per minute.

The preceding CSMP statements, including provisions for the parameters P, SLIFE, and so forth, provisions for obtaining weather observations and provisions for printing the number of infections INF and perhaps other interesting characteristics of the disease, essentially make a simulator of the infection caused by catching *Pseudoperonospora humuli* sporangia. We should now review it generally and in light of the shortcomings that Royle found in a linear equation. In general, spores accumulated on a dry leaf, i.e. SPOR, would cause infections, on the average, after ZTIME plus CTIME plus ITIME hours if the leaf were wetted. This sum is 3 h in the light and $4^{1}/_{2}$ h in the dark. If progress were interrupted by drying, many fungi would perish, and even when misture was continuous some would be lost between stomata, especially when these pores were closed in the dark.

The first shortcoming of the linear equation was that no spores were needed. In the simulator infection is impossible unless sporangia are caught to increase the integral SPOR. The second shortcoming was ignoring sequence, as when rain precedes rather than follows spore catch. In the simulator, wetness before catch is ineffective because progress through the stages is impossible until SPOR has been increased. The third shortcoming was the steady return from hours of rain. In the simulator, brief wetness will be ineffective because essentially no fungi can complete the stages in a short time. The final matter to be corrected is the artifical ignoring of dew and consideration of rain that was required in the prior equation because dew generally fell in the dark when stomata were closed and rain in the daylight when stomata were open to the invaders. In the simulator, dew water is as good as rain water, but in the dark the rate of cyst formation is slow and many are lost between stomata.

Although the simple simulator is intended only as a graphic example, I should mention some facets that appear when it is actually employed for calculation. The calculated average times are shorter than ZTIME, etc. because the necessary ln 2 or 0.7 has been neglected as explained earlier in a footnote. Further the maximum number of zoospores and cysts appear long before the average germination or cyst formation time because they pass so rapidly to the next stage. Finally the boxes of Fig. 40 would have to be subdivided to decrease the scatter in infection time between a few infections after 1 hour to an average infection time of 2.4 h.

This example of hop mildew has now served its purpose of an introduction, differentiating especially (1) an empirical regression equation that summarizes observations and (2) a simulator equation that interprets the observations. Hopefully this contrasting of two mathematical approaches to epidemiology has illuminated the essential nature of a simulator: a logical assembly of information about the constituent parts of an epidemic gleaned from literature, laboratory and field for calculating the course of epidemics. With this introduction made with the generous help of D. J. Royle, I shall now examine the construction of simulators, confess outstanding problems and suggest some uses for simulators.

3. Experimenting to Build a Simulator

The analysis of hop mildew just done has shown that the experiments underlying a simulator are the same as the investigations of pathogen, host and environment that pathologists have long been making because, after all, a simulator is a quantitative integration of our knowledge, a literature survey in a computer program. Thus one must begin with the information found in the "Etiology" in a textbook. If I diagram the life cycle of the pathogen, which has usually been elucidated by a pioneer of a past generation, lo and behold, the flow chart for the computer program or simulator has appeared on my scratch pad.

The next step is determining the impact of environment upon each stage in the life cycle. Since the simulator, like an epidemic itself, is mainly concerned with rates, not levels, information about the dynamics—not statics—of the pathogen is essential, and thus some experiments are useful and others misleading as an example will illustrate.

The curves of Fig. 41 summarize observations of the germination of wet *Alternaria solani* spores at temperatures from 8 to 28°C. If one chose, as often happens, to learn how temperature affects germination by observing it after a fixed time such as 4 h, one would observe the percentages of the circles and dashed line on Fig. 41, and would infer that germination at 8°C was about half as fast as at 28°C. Another worker, observing germination after 2 h, would get the dots and solid curve and say germination at 28°C is infinitely faster than at 8°C. It is true that if leaves were wet for 4 h, fully half as many spores would germinate at cool 8°C as at warm 28°C; but if leaves were wet only 2 h at 8°C, they might as well have never been wet, while at 28°C most of the spores would germinate. The difficulty is, of course, that the dashed curve of Fig. 41 shows the *state* of germination after 4 h, but it does not show the *rate*.

To build a simulator one must, therefore, collect observations such as those of Fig. 42. Dry spores of *A. solani* were wet at time 0, and samples were withdrawn periodically during incubation at 25°C. Germination was nil at 0.5 h, increased quickly to 50% at 1.2 h and eventually reached about 100%. Germination must, of course, be observed similarly at other strategic temperatures. The rate that is essential in simulating germination at 25°C is evident in Fig. 42. Roughly, it is zero for the first half hour, 50% per the next three-quarter hour and then gradually less as the limit of 100% is approached.

The rate or its reciprocal, a characteristic time as employed in the preceding section, brings to attention another criterion of a pertinent experiment: practically there must be a correspondence among the characteristic times of the parts being assembled for the simulator, and a pertinent experiment turns up a time that resembles the other times being assembled. In biology generally, one can conceive a spectrum of characteristic times from the fraction of a second for a biochemical

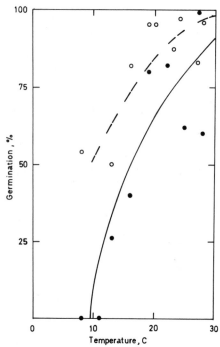

Fig. 41. Germination of wet *Alternaria solani* spores after 2 (●) or 4 (○) h at 8 to 28° C

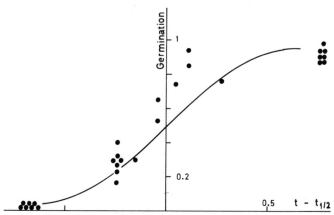

Fig. 42. The course of germination of wet *Alternaria solani* spores at 25° C. The curve is a normal ogive with mean $t_{1/2}$ of 1.22 and standard deviation of 0.39 h. Time is measured in hours from $t_{1/2}$ (WAGGONER and PARLANGE, 1974a)

reaction of molecules, to the minutes for the circulation of protoplasm in a cell, to the hour of germination (Fig. 42), to the days of lesion growth, to the weeks of an epidemic and finally to the years of the succession in plant communities under the impact of disease.

In simulation one attempts to calculate what will happen in one place on the spectrum from knowledge of behavior in another place on the spectrum with shorter—but not very much shorter—characteristic times. In other words, the course of an epidemic with a characteristic time of months might be calculated from knowledge of germination with a characteristic time of hours—but not from knowledge of biochemical reactions in the spore with characteristic times of seconds. Practically, the characteristic times of the constituents of the simulator must be similar and no less than about one thousandth of those of the process being simulated, because the constituent with the shortest time will set the frequency of calculation for the entire simulator. If the characteristic time of a constituent is much shorter than the time of the calculated process, e.g. epidemic, calculation becomes expensive. This orderly progression from short times to longer, but not very much longer times, is also a fundamental matter: "The understanding must not ... be allowed to jump and fly from particulars to remote axioms ... and taking stand upon them as truths that cannot be shaken, proceed to prove and frame the middle axioms by reference to them ... Then only, may we hope well of the sciences, when in a just scale of ascent, and by successive steps not interrupted or broken, we rise from particulars to lesser axioms; and then to middle axioms, one above the other, and last of all to the most general" (Francis Bacon). The spectrum of characteristic times correspond to Bacon's successive steps, and leaping too far causes errors that cannot later be detected and corrected in sequence and with success. Thus having set upon the simulation of a month-long epidemic, only experiments that produce interesting results in a few hours are useful. Experiments completed in minutes or requiring weeks have little use.

Another proviso for a useful experiment is relevance to the epidemic outdoors. Precise application of laboratory results outdoors may be unattainable, but egregious errors can be avoided. Thus the sporulation on established sporophores of *Helminthosporium maydis* goes on fairly rapidly at 10° C on a substrate of filter paper, but it is negligible on maize leaves at that cool temperature (Fig. 43). Surely

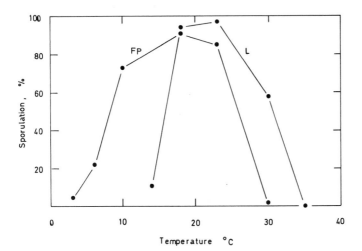

Fig. 43. Sporulation of *Helminthosporium maydis* sporophores in the dark at 2 to 35° C. The curve *FP* represents sporulation on filter paper overnight, and the curve *L* represents sporulation on maize after 2 days (WAGGONER et al., 1972)

the convenient filter paper must be abandoned for the more realistic lesion. Having now illustrated the experiments that must underpin a simulator of the full life cycle of a pathogen and its epidemic, I now illustrate simulators with several examples.

4. Some Simulators

In a review of plant disease prediction from weather data, BOURKE (1970) styled some models of plant disease "full-blooded" because they were "so detailed as to merit being ranked as a simulation of the real thing." These, of course, are the simulators that can be cited here.

The first was a simulator of potato late blight caused by *Phytophthora infestans* (WAGGONER, 1968). In this beginning, essential concepts were evident: (1) treating each fungal stage, e.g. germination, separately and connecting it to the preceding stage and (2) advancing calculation by short increments of simulated time so that all stages of the fungus advanced and were influenced by the environment in essential parallel. An attempt was also made to include the effect of environment on fungicides and of them on the fungus. But the beginning—even if brave—was deficient. A prime purpose of composing a simulator is the guidance to critical experimentation, and the deficiency of the first example was a failure to experiment despite crying needs. Thus the composer of the first simulator merely took the best published values he could find concerning the character of the constituent stages, a defective procedure but an excellent example of the sterility of simulation in an ivory tower. Left in this state, simulation would merit BOURKE'S (1970) sally: "Taking to computers is generally regarded as a sign of maturity in a field of study, in much the same way as experimentation with tobacco and alcohol is a sign that one's children are growing up." Fortunately JAMES (1974) is incorporating the required new experimental results in a simulator of potato late blight.

In the second simulator EPIDEM, which mimicked tomato early blight caused by *Alternaria solani*, the dividend of guidance to essential experiment was cashed in (WAGGONER and HORSFALL, 1969). The development of sporophores, etc. through time in the style of Fig. 42 was observed, revealing the essential rates for the simulator. The consequences of different sequences were investigated: e.g. spores germinated in water are later killed by drying, while those germinated in moist air survive. Crude experiments on the dispersal of spores were also performed because the values of dispersal parameters were critical in the fit of simulation to five seasons of real epidemics.

DE WEILLE (1969) has composed a model, which—although it is not a computer program—was called a simulator by BOURKE (1970) because it has the essential features of calculating the progress of disease from measurements of the behavior of constituent stages. De Weille's model calculates the days on which onion crops are infected by downy mildew conidia, giving special attention to the successive fulfillment of consecutive favorable weather events, a subject emphasized by ROYLE (1973) and by my discussion of Royle's work in a previous section.

A simulator EPIMAY of the Southern corn leaf blight caused by *Helminthosporium maydis* (WAGGONER et al., 1972) followed the pattern set by the simulator of tomato early blight, which disease is caused by a similar fungus. The southern corn leaf blight epidemic of 1970 was caused by a new strain of the pathogen, and North America was faced with a serious plant disease without having at hand a history for estimating the parameters of regression equations or for anticipating how frequently the disease would recur. A simulator was, of course, the natural device for extrapolating to the field the laboratory experiments that were performed over winter. It was also the natural means for assessing the climatic probability of blight by simulating the epidemics corresponding to weather observations of years past and anticipating the favorability for blight as the new season of 1971 unfolded. Fortunately, G. L. Barger was able to marshall the resources of the National Weather Service promptly, and the blight outlook was published weekly according to the observations and simulations of the preceding days (FELCH and BARGER, 1971). Thus EPIMAY was a vehicle for converting laboratory observations into a model of a disease without history and also for forecasting it week by week. Another simulator of this disease is EPICORN composed by L. B. Massie of Pennsylvania State University.

Another simulator EPIVEN, which simulates epidemics of apple scab caused by conidia of *Venturia inaequalis*, demonstrates further simulator adaptability, which derives, of course, from the common foundation of fungal life cycles. After comparing the life cycles of *A. solani* and *V. inaequalis* and modifying EPIDEM accordingly, KRANZ et al. (1973) modified EPIDEM to EPIVEN and successfully simulated epidemics of apple scab.

MYCOS imitates the life cycle of *Mycosphaerella ligulicola* that causes Ascochyta blight of chrysanthemum (McCOY, 1971). Each division of the two-phase disease cycle is considered separately; observed relations between temperature, humidity and cloudiness and the pathogen stages are incorporated in the simulator; and spore dispersal follows physical principles. Disease progress is calculated.

EPIDEMIC is a generalized simulator composed by R. Shrum of Pennsylvania State University. Because a large class of pathogens have similar life cycles, Shrum has been able to compose a flexible simulator that accepts the relations between weather and development for any of the large class and then calculates disease progress for daily, hourly or bihourly observations of environment.

5. Another Sort of Simulator

In his examination of simulators, ZADOKS (1971) suggested that computer languages such as CSMP that are especially designed for simulating the course of changes with time should make the calculation of epidemics less cumbersome and thus more lucid and useful than such Fortran forerunners as EPIDEM. Subsequently WAGGONER and DE WIT (1974) composed a CSMP version of EPIMAY, cutting its complexity and markedly increasing its legibility.

The nature of this more lucid EPIMAY can be described in a few sentences. It is written in CSMP, as is the example of hop mildew in Section 2.4. Its main constituents are integrals or sums as the number of lesions, sporophores and spores per hectare, which are taken without regard to the history or age of the individuals in the sums. The individuals move from integral to integral at rates proportional to the number in the preceding integral. The proportional rates are estimated from

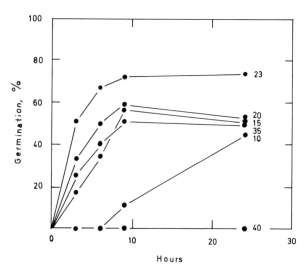

Fig. 44. The course of germination of wet *Helminthosporium maydis* spores at temperatures 10 to 40° C (WAGGONER et al., 1972)

observations as in Fig. 44 and vary with the weather. Where a lag occurs as in the first minutes of Fig. 42, the fungal individuals are put through invisible, intervening stages or integrals. The virtue of the CSMP language is in its directing the composer to rates and its convenience is in its automatically advancing the integrals in parallel as they advance in nature at time intervals that match the changeability of pathogen and weather. Now it is time to pass from this optimism to some hard difficulties that are still outstanding.

6. Difficulties Outstanding

6.1 Virulence and Resistance

Although the lack of explicit treatment of virulence and resistance in simulators might be called a difficulty, it is merely an omission and not an obstacle because many parameters of a simulator are in fact characteristics of a combination of pathogen and host, implicitly incorporating in the simulator the virulence and resistance of the pair.

An example provided by NELSON (1973) illustrates my meaning. In cool weather, pre-1970 populations of race *T* of *Helminthosporium maydis* sporulate significantly less and more slowly than do populations of race *T* collected in the epidemic year of 1970. This difference between races would be simply incorporated in a simulator by different parameters relating sporulation to temperature.

The differences caused by varieties is illustrated by R. J. Lukens. An isolate of race *T* of *H. maydis* was reisolated twice after inoculation of *T*-cytoplasm varieties of maize. Then *T*- and *N*-cytoplasm varieties were inoculated equally, and subsequently an average of 3.2 and 1.8 lesions per leaf appeared and grew to average lengths of 8.0 and 2.2 mm on susceptible and resistant varieties. The procedure for incorporating this difference in resistance into a simulator of blight is clear. In the sections of the simulator concerning inoculation the parameters concerning success would be greater and in the section concerning lesion enlargement the growth rate would be faster for the susceptible than for the resistant variety. Composition of a simulator treating virulence and resistance requires the composer to learn which stages are affected by virulence and resistance and in what environment, and then incorporate this knowledge into the calculation.

6.2 Absolute Numbers

Simulators so far composed generally have an initial condition of an assumed number such as 10 lesions or 100 spores that multiply according to the weather without regard for (1) the decreasing supply of healthy tissue to attack or (2) the escape or arrival of spores across the boundaries of the simulated system. Such simulators essentially transform weather data into the potential for disease according to the physiology of the pathogen. The simulators may have successfully distinguished relatively light from relatively severe seasons of disease, but they have generally not calculated absolute numbers as 10 million lesions involving 2% of the 400 million cm^2 of foliage on a hectare of land on August 15. KRANZ et al. (1973) identified this difficulty of calculating absolute numbers as "the question of a reference basis or dimension", and it deserves attention.

The difficulty of the fungus that kills all its host and has no place to go can be dealt with in the manner associated with the "multiple infection transformation." Long ago W. R. Thompson (GREGORY, 1948) solved the problem of how infection would increase when parasites landed upon already-infected hosts and thus failed: the increase in infestation would be proportional to the proportion of the hosts that were still healthy. This concept was easily incorporated into the simulator EPIMAY (WAGGONER et al., 1972): The simulated system was defined as a hectare, and the area of lesions grown from the initial infection was simulated as before except that infection was modified by multiplying by the probability of a spore landing on healthy tissue. The probability was simply the total foliage area on the hectare less the lesion area divided by the total foliage areas which was 1 hectare times the leaf area index. This correctly causes the infection per spore to decline to zero as the limit of total infection of the foliage area is approached, solves the problem of multiple infection, and starkly exposes the remainder of the difficulty in correctly calculating absolute numbers.

The remainder of the difficulty is knowing how many fungi are initially in the hectare, how many are lost by falling on the soil or blowing away, and how many arrive from afar. In analyzing one stage of hop mildew in Section 2.3. I began with the observed spores in the air, which I said was a considerable advantage, but in simulating an entire fungal cycle the number of those air-borne spores must be calculated. It is fair to ask that the spores from outside the system be furnished to the simulator, but the worth of the simulator depends upon its calculating the spores that are carried into the air or even into rain from the hectare of the simulator. Rational rules for the removal of spores and their dilution in the wind and rain have been incorporated in simulators, but the rules and their parameters are both uncertain and important in calculating the absolute number of infections (WAGGONER et al., 1972). Until the requisite biological and meteorological knowledge of dispersal is acquired, we shall continue encountering the difficulties that SHANER et al. (1972) found in comparing the output of EPIMAY to observations of the absolute percentage of infection in corn fields through the length of Indiana, and BOURKE (1970) can justly continue complaining that simulation successes are mere predictions of the general rise of infection with time.

6.3 Unsteady Environment

Outdoors, weather changes in infinite variety, while practically the experimenter must measure the response of an organism to a few defined and usually steady environments. For example, germination at steady temperatures can be observed and curves compiled for the range of temperatures encountered outdoors (Fig. 44). One is then left with employing these observations at steady temperature to calculate germination in a changeable environment outdoors, and has no guide to the effect of brief exposure to temperatures that prevent germination.

The simplest procedure neglects history and assumes that development depends only upon the present stage of development and the current environment. Thus ROWE and POWELSON (1973) succeeded in calculating the quantity of sporulation of *Cercosporella herpotrichoides* after two weeks of variable temperatures by assigning the variable temperatures indices derived from experiments at steady temperatures. In another example, the simulator EPIMAY would calculate the germination of *H. maydis* (Fig. 44) at $10°$ C for three hours as 0%, and then if the temperature warmed to $23°$ C in the next three hours, germination would be calculated as 50%. This is a plausible procedure, but it goes against the experience that history seems to matter, as shown by two examples: (1) exposing *Alternaria solani* spores to $45°$ C can quadruple the subsequent time for germination at $25°$ C (WAGGONER and PARLANGE, 1974a) even though spores do not germinate at a steady $45°$ C, and (2) exposing *H. maydis* to 10 or $35°$ C for a day drastically decreases subsequent production of sporophores (WAGGONER et al., 1972).

The problem of development in an unsteady environment has been tackled by WAGGONER and PARLANGE (1974a, 1974b) who devised a scheme for calculating the germination of *Alternaria solani* spores in variable temperature. They began by conceiving development of germ tubes as a dangerous journey of f steps or boxes taken at a rate P per hour between initial wetting and final germination where f, P and the mortality rate B vary with the environment (Fig. 45). The steps might be physical changes or they might be levels of an essential compound produced on the way to germination. Since P is made the same between all boxes for a given environment, the boxes are equal periods along the journey. When imaginary spores journey through many boxes at a steady temperature and thus at a constant rate P, the number safely reaching the destination of a germ tube increases with time as the cumulative normal curve in Fig. 42. Real spores germinate up to about 90% as the cumulative normal curve (COCHRANE, 1958).

Mathematically, PARLANGE (1974) showed that the eventual proportion H germinating was approximately

$$H = \exp(-B\,t_{1/2})$$

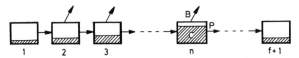

Fig. 45. A box model of development. Spores pass through f stages on their way to germination. The number C represented by the level of shading in each box changes as the fraction P per hour moves forward, while the fraction B per hour dies (WAGGONER and PARLANGE, 1974a)

where $t_{1/2}$ is the time for $H/2$ to germinate. If things go well, B will be zero, H will be 1, and $t_{1/2}$ will be the time for half the original spores to germinate. Completing the specification of the curve of germination, Parlange located the curve by $t_{1/2}$:

$$t_{1/2} = f/P .$$

Then, since a cumulative normal curve represents the course of germination fairly well, the rise in germination was specified by the variance:

$$s^2 = f/P^2 .$$

The standard deviation is a measure of the variation of individual germination times, and it is also the time for germination to increase from 16 to 50% or from 50 to 84%. Although I have shown how the course of germination is estimated from the characteristics of the process diagramed in Fig. 45, the equations can, of course, be turned around, estimating the characteristics f, P and B from observations of the H, $t_{1/2}$, and s^2 of the germination curve.

Experimentally, from 10 to 29 C, WAGGONER and PARLANGE (1974b) observed that (1) f was constant and (2) P increased proportionally to the temperature T above a threshold T_0:

$$P = f/t_{1/2} = a(T - T_0).$$

where a is a constant of proportionality.

Now we come to the goal of calculating development at variable temperatures. PARLANGE (1974) has shown that when f is fairly large, $t_{1/2}$ is simply the time when the varying $P(t)$ add to f:

$$f \simeq \int_0^{t_{1/2}} P(t)\, dt$$

If P is constant, this equation reduces to the equation between $t_{1/2}$ and f/P given earlier for steady temperature. The variance at variable temperature is

$$s^2 \simeq f/P(t_{1/2})^2$$

where $P(t_{1/2})$ is the rate for the temperature prevailing at $t_{1/2}$.

When the spores at variable temperature promptly take on the same rates P that they would have had at the same constant temperatures, the $P(t)$ and $P(t_{1/2})$ are easily obtained from experiments at steady temperatures. In the case of *Alternaria* spores at 10 to 19°C, f was observed to be constant and P was equal to $a(T - T_0)$; hence

$$f \simeq \int_0^{t_{1/2}} a(T - T_0)\, dt \quad \text{or}$$

$$\text{constant} \simeq \int_0^{t_{1/2}} (T - T_0)\, dt.$$

The latter is the familiar heat-sum way of calculating development, essentially begun by Reaumur in the 18th Century.

Turning briefly to another organism, *Phragmidium mucronatum* urediospores, one finds f is constant and P increases linearly with temperature from only 9 to 15°C (COCHRANE, 1945). It is significant that the disease caused by this fungus is favored by cool temperatures.

The foregoing rules for the $t_{1/2}$ and s^2 of the germination curve were tested by comparing predicted and observed values for *Alternaria* spores germinating at temperatures varying from 10 to 29°C, where germination is eventually about 100%. The test was passed, indicating that the spores have the same P at steady and variable temperatures and establishing a means of calculating the entire course of germination in a temperate, variable environment from simple observations in steady environments. This outcome corresponds to the frequent success of the heat-sum calculation of development time (i.e. $t_{1/2}$) — plus a calculation of the shape of the germination curve.

The remaining problem—an important one—is calculating development outside the temperate range. Since exposing wet *Alternaria* spores to 4°C before exposure to the temperate range speeded germination slightly more than anticipated from the P at steady 4°C, a faster P is needed for such a prior exposure. This P can be deduced from experiments at varying temperature.

Now what happens at lethally hot temperatures? Spores of *Alternaria* were heated to 45°C and cooled back to 25°C (WAGGONER and PARLANGE, 1974a). A fraction of B died each hour, and this was estimated from the proportion of the spores that eventually germinated after they returned to 25°C. In the case of *A. solani* and fluctuations between 25 and 45°C, the outcome was relatively simple. The mortality B increased with the stage of development, i.e., how long the spore had developed at 25°C before heating to 45°C. The rate P at 45°C was much faster than at 25°C, especially when development was well advanced, but germination was nevertheless delayed by an accompanying increase in the number of stages f to be accomplished. The rate at 25°C was the same before and after exposure to 45°C, just as the spores at variable moderate temperatures promptly took on the same rates that they would have had at the same steady temperatures. This calculation could proceed even with variation to hot temperatures from a knowledge of present environment and stages of development. Only the evidence of germination or failure is available, but one can speculate that heating to 45°C denatures and kills some spores, while in other spores the same heating both speeds reaction of the essential compound as it does in *in vitro* chemistry and simultaneously destroys something, leaving the spores further from their goal of germination after their spell of heating. Although other organisms and environments will undoubtedly have different outcomes, the conception of Fig. 45 with its speeding but dying hot spores and its tie between the mean and variance of germination time does fit the germination of *A. solani* spores in both a variable temperate and intemperate environment and gives hope that controlled experiments can eventually be a foundation for calculations about an unsteady outdoors.

6.4 Testing

Although simulators have usually been tested, their tests have not been sufficiently critical because the many parameters in the model can easily be fudged to fit the few data. Nevertheless some progress has been made.

Rudimentary testing can be illustrated by the case of EPIDEM (WAGGONER and HORSFALL, 1969). When the testing of EPIDEM got underway, most of its parameters had been set *a priori* by laboratory observations, but two concerning dispersal by wind and rain remained unknown. Nevertheless, when plausible values were assigned to these two, the relative severity of disease during three seasons was mimicked, and even an irregular increase in one season was simulated. Further the relative severity between a separate pair of years with another variety of host was accurately obtained. This test certainly establishes the relevance to the field of the laboratory work organized in the simulator, but one must also admit that two parameters were not set *a priori,* there were only 11 observations in the five years, and relative rather than absolute numbers were compared.

Tests of later simulators have employed comparisons of absolute numbers and hence been more critical. KRANZ et al. (1973) simulated the absolute number of scab lesions on 100 apple leaves successfully, but they emphasized that their success was founded upon a fortunate choice of values for some poorly known parameters. The absolute numbers in the explosive onset of southern corn leaf blight were also simulated, but this success required an *a posteriori* adjustment of two parameters concerning dispersal (WAGGONER et al., 1972). (One must not be too harsh on the simulator for a little juggling of parameters, of course, because that is all that a statistician ever hopes to do with regression equations!)

A remarkably large and prompt test of a simulator of southern corn leaf blight was undertaken in the first year after its outbreak in North America. The test was led by G. L. Barger of the U.S. Environmental Data Service and several scientists at Purdue University. Cooperators in 12 states and Ontario provided weather observations weekly, calculations were made by L. A. Joos, and the results were promptly published. Figure 46 shows the agreement between the simulated (ordinate) and observed (abscissa) increase in blight in the Indiana portion of the network, and FELCH and BARGER (1971) concluded that the simulator "is a fully operational program which gives a reasonable estimate (where blight) was developing most rapidly."

When the Indiana experience was examined further, SHANER et al. (1972) found logical reasons for the outcomes in two localities that were poorly simulated: in one resistant corn was grown, and in the other foreign weather data had had to be used.

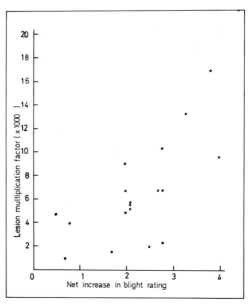

Fig. 46. The relation between the simulated lesion multiplication factor and the observed increase in rating of southern corn leaf blight at stations from northern to southern Indiana between mid-July and mid-August, 1971 (FELCH and BARGER, 1971)

At the other four stations examined, the logarithmic rate of blight increase simulated for the corn fields was within a satisfying 5% of the actual rate of increase observed during 35 midsummer days. After this success in calculating the rates of increase, SHANER et al. (1972) went on to simulate the absolute area of leaves diseased on given dates. After incorporating in the simulator the actual initial disease at different initial times related to different planting dates, and after considering immigrant spores from afar, they succeeded. Thus, the testing of simulators seems a difficulty that will eventually be removed.

The concluding remark regarding testing must emphasize how to compose a simulator so that it (1) requires a minimum of testing, (2) provides many criteria for testing, and (3) can be modified systematically. These are all accomplished by building with parts that have a physical meaning. Consider EPIMAY. It has about a dozen parameters and 30 curves relating behavior of an organism to environment. It would have been absurd to think that a simple comparison of a few observations of an epidemic against the number of lesions calculated by the entire EPIMAY simulator would tell much about the accuracy of one parameter buried in the simulator. Instead of depending on such a test alone the constituent parameters and curves were all assigned physical meanings—e.g., spores per mm^2 of lesion—and they were tested *a priori* by observing a single stage of the pathogenesis, leaving only a mimimum although important final testing for the entire simulator. Because the simulator is composed of realistic parts, such as sporulation or spore dispersal, many critical tests can be made, e.g. requiring that the number of spores on the lesions or in the air be mimicked along with the increase in the lesions. Finally, when a logical simulator fails or new information is obtained regarding any portion of the pathogenic cycle, the simulator can be improved, systematically and piece-by-piece, without losing the ground gained by an early but logical simulator.

7. Use of Simulators

Projecting uses for accurate simulators is easier than making them, and this con-cluding subject can be briefly treated. As the simulator is assembled it has all the usefulness of any ordering of scattered results concerning the parts of an event as complex as an epidemic; it is a guide to what is relevant and what is not, to what is known to an adequate and what to a ridiculous precision. When the simulator is being tested it provides a check list of factors that need measuring and factors that are of secondary importance. A proven simulator can provide the benefits of a disease forecast (BOURKE, 1970), and even during its first use in the field, a logical simulator "helped prevent any over-reaction to the (blight) threat ... and provided an immediate, at least tentative, reason for the escape of most of the crop ..." (FELCH and BARGER, 1971). Finally because the simulator has realistic parts, a characteristic such as hardiness of spores, frequency of irrigation or susceptibility of the host to penetration can be modified in the simulator, and then the conse-quent effect upon epidemics in many years of weather promptly examined.

References

ANALYTIS,S.: Methodik der Analyse von Epidemien dargestellt am Apfelschorf (*Venturia inae-qualis* [Cooke] Aderh.). Acta Phytomedica 1, 1–76 (1973).

BOURKE,P.M.A.: Use of weather information in the prediction of plant epiphytotics. Ann. Rev. Phytopath. 8, 345–370 (1970).

BURLEIGH,J.R., EVERSMEYER,M.G., ROELFS,A.P.: Development of linear equations for pre-dicting wheat leaf rust. Phytopathology 62, 947–953 (1972).

COCHRANE,V.W.: The common leaf rust of cultivated roses caused by *Phragmidium mucrona-tum* (Fr.) Schlecht. Cornell Univ. Agr. Exp. Mem. 268 (1945).

COCHRANE,V.W.: Physiology of fungi. New York: John Wiley and Sons 1958.

FELCH,R.E., BARGER,G.L.: EPIMAY and southern corn leaf blight. Weekly Weather Crop Bull. 58 (43), 13–17 (1971).

GREGORY,P.H.: The multiple infection transformation. Ann. appl. Biol. 35, 412–417 (1948).

GREGORY,P.H.: Microbiology of the atmosphere. London: Leonard Hill 1961.

IBM: System / 360 continuous system modeling program users manual H 20–03 67–3, 1969.

JAMES,W.C.: Assessment of plant disease incidence, severity and losses. Ann. Rev. Phytopath. (In press 1974).

KRANZ,J., MOGK,M., STUMPF,A.: EPIVEN—ein Simulator für Apfelschorf. Z. Pflanzen-krankh. 80, 181–187 (1973).

McCOY,R.E.: Epidemiology of chrysanthemum *Ascochyta* blight. Ph.D. Thesis, Cornell Univ., Ithaca, N.Y. (1971).

NELSON,R.R.: Pathogen variation and host resistance. In: Breeding plants for disease resist-ance: concepts and applications (ed. R.R.NELSON), pp.40–48. University Park: Penn. State U. Press 1973.

PARLANGE,J.-Y.: Analytic solution to model passages through phenophases. In: Phenology and seasonality modeling (ed. H.LIETH). Berlin-Heidelberg-New York:Springer (In press, 1974).

ROWE, R. C., POWELSON, R. L.: Epidemiology of *Cercosporella* foot rot of wheat. I. Spore production. Phytopathology, 981–984 (1973).

ROYLE, D. J.: Infection periods in relation to the natural development of hop downy mildew (*Pseudoperonospora humuli*). Ann. appl. Biol. **66**, 281–291 (1970).

ROYLE, D. J.: Quantitative relationships between infection by the hop downy mildew pathogen, *Pseudoperonospora humuli*, and weather and inoculum factors. Ann. appl. Biol. **73**, 19–30 (1973).

ROYLE, D. J., THOMAS, G. G.: The influence of stomatal opening on the infection of hop leaves by *Pseudoperonospora humuli*. Physiol. Plant Path. **1**, 329–343 (1971 a).

ROYLE, D. J., THOMAS, G. G.: Observations with the scanning electron microscope on the early stages of hop leaf infection by *Pseudoperonospora humuli*. Physiol. Plant Path. **1**, 345–349 (1971 b).

ROYLE, D. J., THOMAS, G. G.: Factors affecting zoospore responses towards stomata in hop downy mildew *(Pseudoperonospora humuli)* including some comparisons with grapevine downy mildew *(Plasmopara viticola)*. Physiol. Plant Path. **3**, 405–417 (1973).

SHANER, G. E., PEART, R. M., NEWMAN, J. E., STIRM, W. L., LOEWER, O. L.: EPIMAY an evaluation of a plant disease display model. Purdue Univ. Agr. Exp. Sta. RB-**890** (1972).

SONODA, R. M., OGAWA, J. M.: Ecological factors limiting epidemics of hop downy mildew in arid climates. Hilgardia **41**, (15), 457–474 (1972).

VAN DER PLANK, J. E.: Plant diseases: epidemics and control. New York: Academic Press 1963.

WAGGONER, P. E.: Weather and the rise and fall of fungi. In: Biometeorology (ed. W. P. LOWRY), pp. 45–66. Corvallis: Oregon State Univ. Press 1968.

WAGGONER, P. E., DE WIT, C. T.: Growth and development of *Helminthosporium maydis*. In: Simulation of ecological processes (ed. C. T. DE WIT and J. GOUDRIAN), pp. 99–123. Wageningen: PUDOC 1974.

WAGGONER, P. E., HORSFALL, J. G.: EPIDEM, a simulator of plant disease written for a computer. Conn. Agr. Exp. Sta. Bull. **698** (1969).

WAGGONER, P. E., HORSFALL, J. G., LUKENS, R. J.: EPIMAY, a simulator of southern corn leaf blight. Conn. Agr. Exp. Sta. Bull. **729** (1972).

WAGGONER, P. E., PARLANGE, J.-Y.: Mathematical model for spore germination at changing temperature. Phytopathology **64**, 605–610 (1974a).

WAGGONER, P. E., PARLANGE, J.-Y.: Verification of a model of spore germination at variable, moderate temperatures. Phytopathology (In press 1974b).

DE WEILLE, G. A.: A climatological model typifying the days on which onion crops get infected by downy mildew conidia. Fifth Int. Biometeorol. Congress Proc. Biometeorology **4** (II), 198 (1969).

ZADOKS, J. C.: Systems analysis and the dynamics of epidemics. Phytopathology **61**, 600–610 (1971).

ZATTLER, F.: Über die Einflüsse von Temperatur und Luftfeuchtigkeit auf Keimung und Fruktifikation von *Pseudoperonospora humuli* und auf das Zustandekommen der Infektion des Hopfens. Phytopath. Z. **3**, 281–302 (1931).

Subject Index

Ecological Studies
Analysis and Synthesis
Editors: J. Jacobs,
O.L. Lange, J.S. Olson,
W. Wieser

Distribution rights for
U.K., Commonwealth,
and the Traditional
British Market
(excluding Canada):
Chapman & Hall
Ltd. London

Vol. 1:
**Analysis of Temperate
Forest Ecosystems**
First corrected reprint
Editor: D.E. Reichle
91 figs. XII, 304 pages
1973. Cloth DM 52,—
US $21.30
ISBN 3-540-04793-X

Vol. 2:
**Integrated Experimental
Ecology**
Methods and Results of
Ecosystem Research in
the German Solling
Project
Editor: H. Ellenberg
53 figs. XX, 214 pages
1971. Cloth DM 58,—;
US $23.70
ISBN 3-540-05074-4

Vol. 3:
**The Biology of the
Indian Ocean**
Editor: B. Zeitzschel in
cooperation with
S.A. Gerlach
286 figs. XIII, 549 pages
1973. Cloth DM 123,—
US $50.20
ISBN 3-540-06004-9

Vol. 4:
**Physical Aspects of Soil
Water and Salts
in Ecosystems**
Editors: A. Hadas;
D. Swartzendruber;
P.E. Rijtema; M. Fuchs;
B. Yaron
221 figs. 61 tab.
XVI, 460 pages. 1973

Cloth DM 94,—;
US $38.40
ISBN 3-540-06109-6

Vol. 5:
Arid Zone Irrigation
Editors: B. Yaron;
E. Danfors; Y. Vaadia
181 figs. X, 434 pages
1973. Cloth DM 94,—
US $38.40
ISBN 3-540-06206-8

Vol. 6:
K. Stern, L. Roche:
**Genetics of Forest
Ecosystems**
70 figs. X, 330 pages
1974. Cloth DM 72,—;
US $29.40
ISBN 3-540-06095-2

Vol. 7:
**Mediterranean Type
Ecosystems**
Origin and Structure
Editors: F. di Castri;
H.A. Mooney
88 figs. XII, 405 pages
1973. Cloth DM 78,—
US $31.90
ISBN 3-540-06106-1

Vol. 8:
**Phenology and
Seasonality Modeling**
Editor: H. Lieth
120 figs. App
Approx. 350 pages
1974. Cloth DM 117,20;
US $47.80
ISBN 3-540-06524-5

Vol. 9: B. Slavík:
**Methods of Studying
Plant Water Relations**
With contributions by
B. Slavík, J. Čatský,
J. Solárová,
H.R. Oppenheimer,
J. Hrbáček, J. Slaviková,
V. Kozinka, U. Úlehla,,
P.G. Jarvis, M.S. Jarvis
181 figs. XVIII,
449 pages. 1974
Cloth DM 76,—; US $31.10
ISBN 3-540-06686-1

Springer-Verlag has the
exclusive distribution
rights for the English
edition in all countries
excluding the Socialist
countries.

Vol. 10:
**Coupling of Land and
Water Systems**
Editor: A.D. Hasler
Approx. 95 figs.
Approx. 350 pages. 1974
Cloth DM 60,80;
US $24.90
ISBN 3-540-06707-8

Vol. 11:
**Tropical Ecological
Systems: Trends in
Terrestrial and Aquatic
Research**
Editors: F.B. Golley,
E. Medina
Approx. 127 figs.
Approx. 385 pages. 1974
Cloth DM 60,80;
US $24.90
ISBN 3-540-06706-X

Vol. 12:
**Perspectives of
Biophysical Ecology**
Editors: D.M. Gates,
R.B. Schmerl
Approx. 210 figs. 1974
Cloth DM 85,30;
US $34.80
ISBN 3-540-06743-4

Prices are subject to change
without notice

**Springer-Verlag
Berlin
Heidelberg
New York**

Oecologia

In Cooperation with the International Association
for Ecology (Intecol)

Editorial Board: L.C. Birch, Sydney; L.C. Bliss,
Edmonton; P. Buchner, Porto D'Ischia; D.M. Gates,
Ann Arbor, Mich.; J.J. Gilbert, Hanover, N.H.; J. Jacobs,
Munich; T. Kira, Osaka; O.L. Lange, Würzburg;
H. Löffler, Vienna; D. Neumann, Cologne; I. Phillipson,
Oxford; H. Remmert (Managing Editor), Erlangen;
F. Schaller, Vienna; K.E.F. Watt, Davis, Calif.; W. Wieser,
Innsbruck; C.T. de Wit, Wageningen; H. Ziegler, Munich

Oecologia reflects the dynamically growing interest in
ecology. Emphasis is placed on the functional interrela-
tionship of organisms and environment rather than on
morphological adaptation. The journal publishes original
articles, short communications, and symposium reports
on all aspects of modern ecology, with particular reference
to physiological and experimental ecology, population
ecology, organic production, and mathematical models.

Fields of Interest: Autecology, Physiological Ecology,
Theoretical Ecology, Population Genetics, Population
Dynamics, Demography, Behavioral Ecology,
Epidemiology, Zoology, Botany, Agriculture, Forestry,
Pest Control

Subscription information and sample copies upon request

Springer-Verlag
Berlin Heidelberg New York